Succeed

Eureka Math®
Grade 1
Module 1

TEKS EDITION

Great Minds® is the creator of *Eureka Math*®, *Wit & Wisdom*®, *Alexandria Plan*™, and *PhD Science*®.

Published by Great Minds PBC.
greatminds.org

Copyright © 2021 Great Minds PBC. Except where otherwise noted, this content is published under a limited public license with the Texas Education Agency. Use limited to Non-Commercial educational purposes. For more information, visit https://gm.greatminds.org/texas.

Printed in the USA
1 2 3 4 5 6 7 8 9 10 CCR 25 24 23 22 21

ISBN 978-1-64929-627-6

Learn ♦ Practice ♦ Succeed

Eureka Math® student materials for *A Story of Units*® (K–5) are available in the *Learn, Practice, Succeed* trio. This series supports differentiation and remediation while keeping student materials organized and accessible. Educators will find that the *Learn, Practice,* and *Succeed* series also offers coherent—and therefore, more effective—resources for Response to Intervention (RTI), extra practice, and summer learning.

Learn

Eureka Math Learn serves as a student's in-class companion where they show their thinking, share what they know, and watch their knowledge build every day. *Learn* assembles the daily classwork—Application Problems, Exit Tickets, Problem Sets, templates—in an easily stored and navigated volume.

Practice

Each *Eureka Math* lesson begins with a series of energetic, joyous fluency activities, including those found in *Eureka Math Practice.* Students who are fluent in their math facts can master more material more deeply. With *Practice,* students build competence in newly acquired skills and reinforce previous learning in preparation for the next lesson.

Together, *Learn* and *Practice* provide all the print materials students will use for their core math instruction.

Succeed

Eureka Math Succeed enables students to work individually toward mastery. These additional problem sets align lesson by lesson with classroom instruction, making them ideal for use as homework or extra practice. Each problem set is accompanied by a Homework Helper, a set of worked examples that illustrate how to solve similar problems.

Teachers and tutors can use *Succeed* books from prior grade levels as curriculum-consistent tools for filling gaps in foundational knowledge. Students will thrive and progress more quickly as familiar models facilitate connections to their current grade-level content.

Students, families, and educators:

Thank you for being part of the *Eureka Math*® community, where we celebrate the joy, wonder, and thrill of mathematics.

Nothing beats the satisfaction of success—the more competent students become, the greater their motivation and engagement. The *Eureka Math Succeed* book provides the guidance and extra practice students need to shore up foundational knowledge and build mastery with new material.

What is in the Succeed *book?*

Eureka Math Succeed books deliver supported practice sets that parallel the lessons of *A Story of Units*®. Each *Succeed* lesson begins with a set of worked examples, called *Homework Helpers*, that illustrate the modeling and reasoning the curriculum uses to build understanding. Next, students receive scaffolded practice through a series of problems carefully sequenced to begin from a place of confidence and add incremental complexity.

How should Succeed *be used?*

The collection of *Succeed* books can be used as differentiated instruction, practice, homework, or intervention. When coupled with *Affirm*®, *Eureka Math*'s digital assessment system, *Succeed* lessons enable educators to give targeted practice and to assess student progress. *Succeed*'s perfect alignment with the mathematical models and language used across *A Story of Units* ensures that students feel the connections and relevance to their daily instruction, whether they are working on foundational skills or getting extra practice on the current topic.

Where can I learn more about Eureka Math *resources?*

The Great Minds® team is committed to supporting students, families, and educators with an ever-growing library of resources, available at eureka-math.org. The website also offers inspiring stories of success in the *Eureka Math* community. Share your insights and accomplishments with fellow users by becoming a *Eureka Math* Champion.

Best wishes for a year filled with Eureka moments!

Jill Diniz
Director of Mathematics
Great Minds

Contents

Module 1: Sums and Differences to 10

Topic A: Embedded Numbers and Decompositions
Lesson 1 1
Lesson 2 5
Lesson 3 9

Topic B: Counting On from Embedded Numbers
Lesson 4 13
Lesson 5 17
Lesson 6 21
Lesson 7 25
Lesson 8 31

Topic C: Addition Word Problems
Lesson 9 35
Lesson 10 39
Lesson 11 45
Lesson 12 49
Lesson 13 53

Topic D: Strategies for Counting On
Lesson 14 57
Lesson 15 61
Lesson 16 65

Topic E: The Commutative Property of Addition and the Equal Sign
Lesson 17 69
Lesson 18 73
Lesson 19 77
Lesson 20 81

Topic F: Development of Addition Fluency Within 10

Lesson 21 85

Lesson 22 89

Lesson 23 93

Lesson 24 97

Topic G: Subtraction as an Unknown Addend Problem

Lesson 25 101

Lesson 26 105

Lesson 27 109

Topic H: Subtraction Word Problems

Lesson 28 113

Lesson 29 117

Lesson 30 121

Lesson 31 125

Lesson 32 129

Topic I: Decomposition Strategies for Subtraction

Lesson 33 133

Lesson 34 137

Lesson 35 141

Lesson 36 145

Lesson 37 149

Topic J: Development of Subtraction Fluency Within 10

Lesson 38 153

Lesson 39 157

A STORY OF UNITS – TEKS EDITION

Lesson 1 Homework Helper

1•1

1. Circle 5. Then, make a number bond.

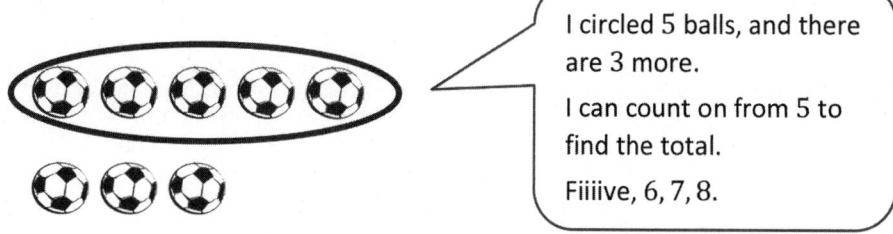

I circled 5 balls, and there are 3 more.

I can count on from 5 to find the total.

Fiiiive, 6, 7, 8.

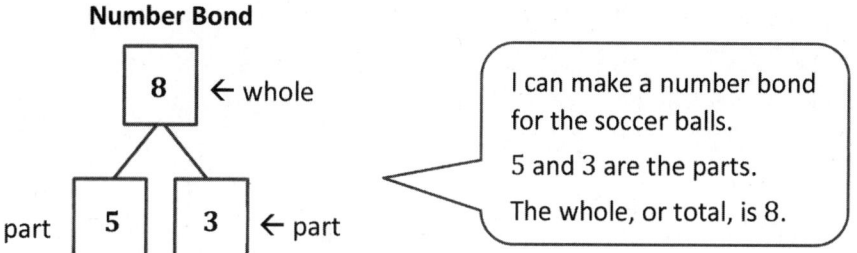

I can make a number bond for the soccer balls.

5 and 3 are the parts.

The whole, or total, is 8.

2. Make a number bond for the domino.

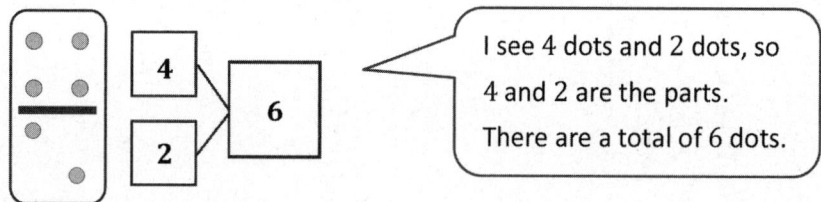

I see 4 dots and 2 dots, so 4 and 2 are the parts.

There are a total of 6 dots.

Lesson 1: Analyze and describe embedded numbers (to 10) using 5-groups and number bonds.

© Great Minds PBC
TEKS Edition | greatminds.org/texas

A STORY OF UNITS – TEKS EDITION   Lesson 1 Homework 1•1

Name _____   Date _____

Circle 5, and then make a number bond.

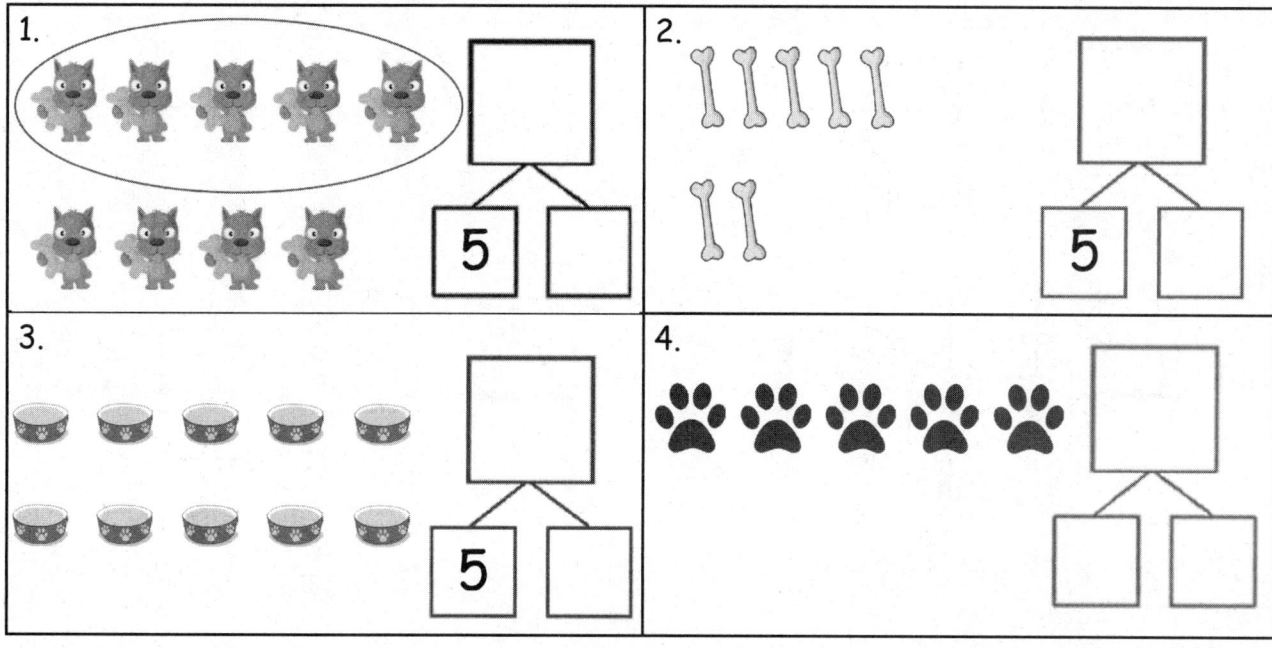

Make a number bond that shows 5 as one part.

5.
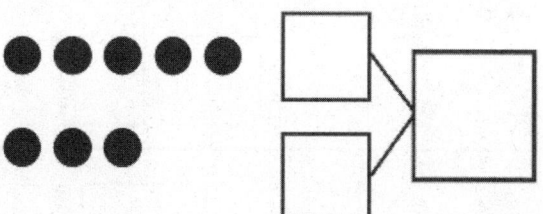

6.
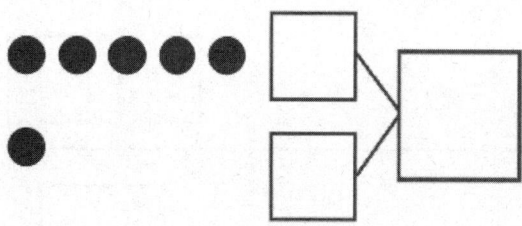

7.
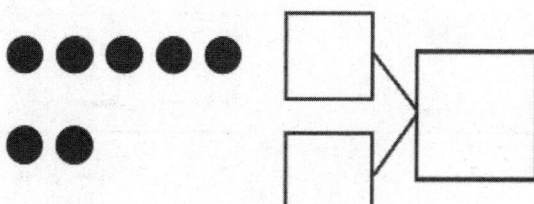

8.
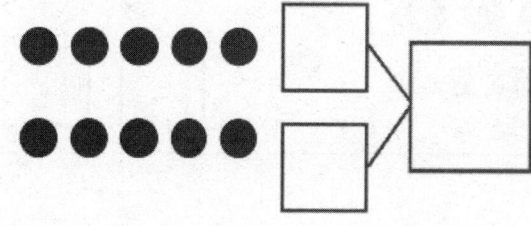

Lesson 1: Analyze and describe embedded numbers (to 10) using 5-groups and number bonds.

A STORY OF UNITS – TEKS EDITION
Lesson 1 Homework 1•1

Make a number bond for the dominoes.

9.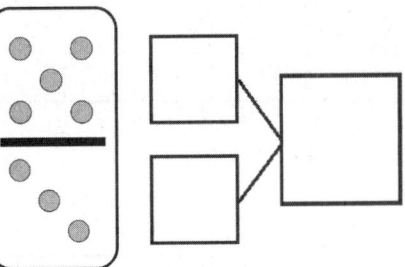

10.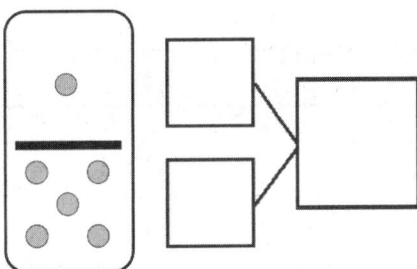

11.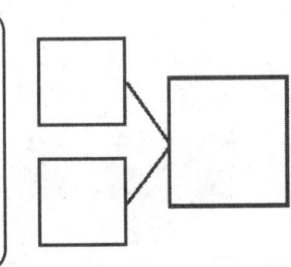

12.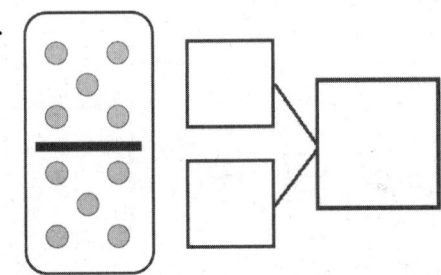

Circle 5 and count. Then, make a number bond.

13.

14.

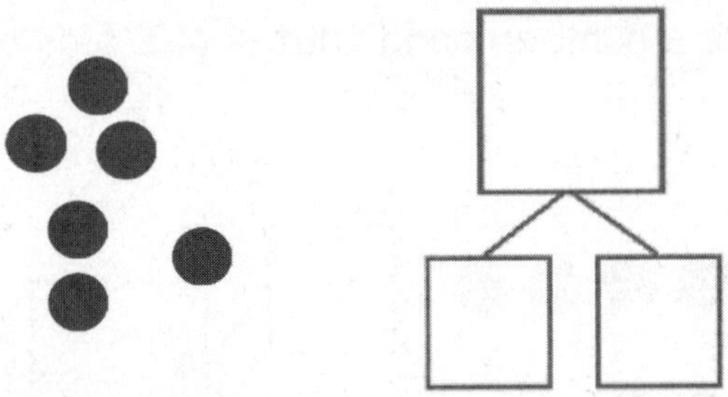

15.

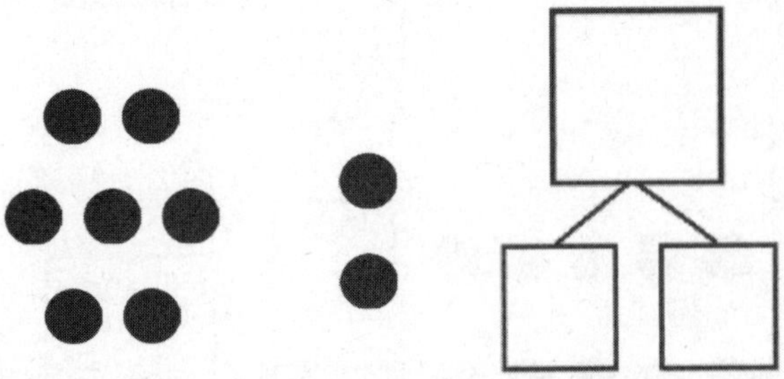

16.

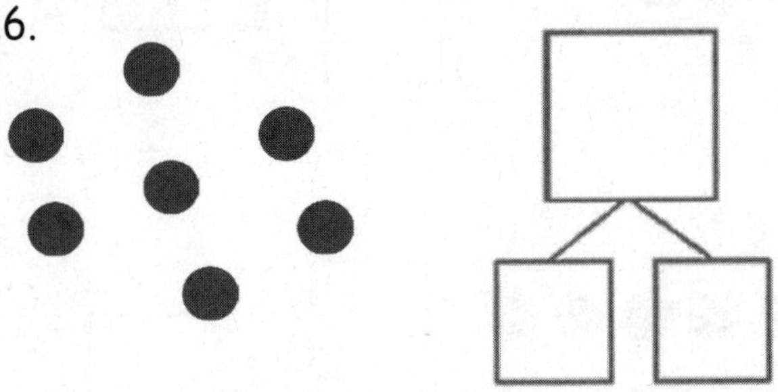

Lesson 1: Analyze and describe embedded numbers (to 10) using 5-groups and number bonds.

A STORY OF UNITS – TEKS EDITION   Lesson 2 Homework Helper 1•1

1. Circle 2 parts you see. Make a number bond to match.

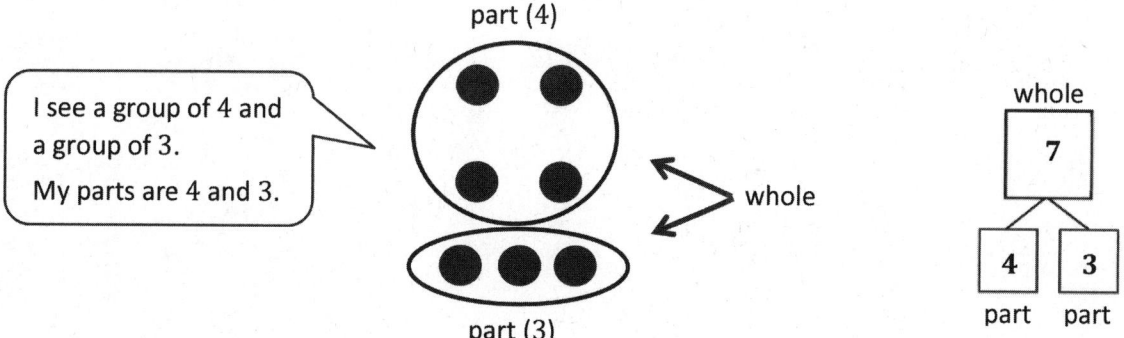

2. How many fruits do you see? Write at least 2 different number bonds to show different ways to break apart the total.

Lesson 2: Reason about embedded numbers in varied configurations using number bonds.

5

A STORY OF UNITS – TEKS EDITION Lesson 2 Homework 1•1

Name _____ Date _____

Circle 2 parts you see. Make a number bond to match.

1.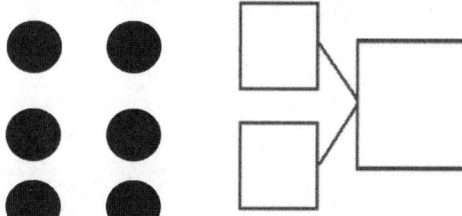

2.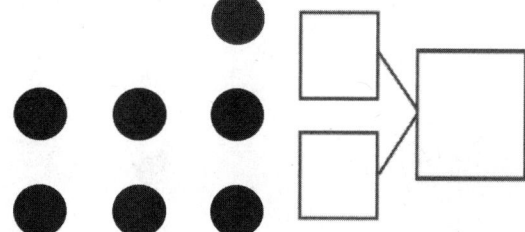

3.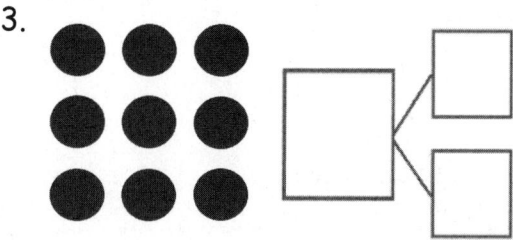

4.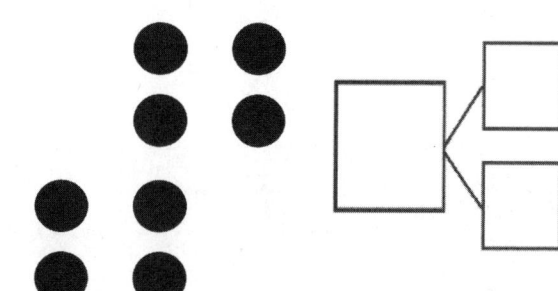

5.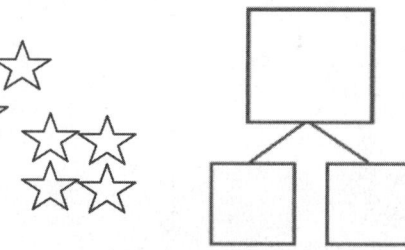

6.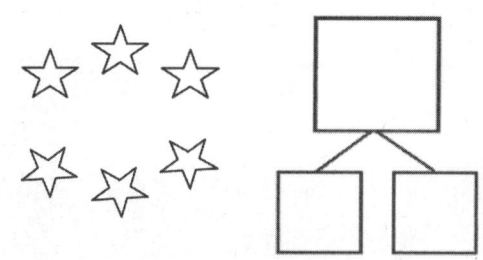

7.

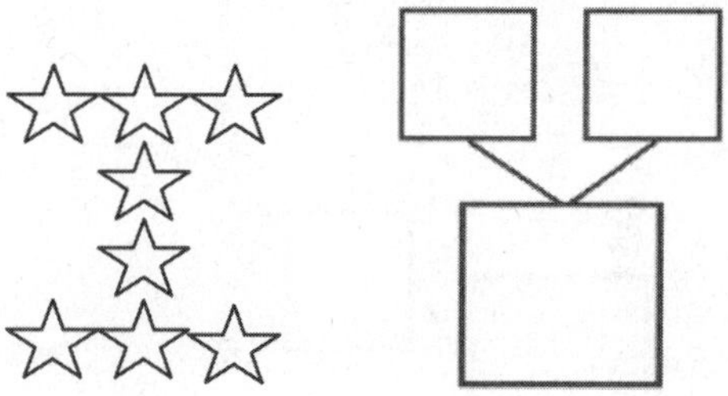

8.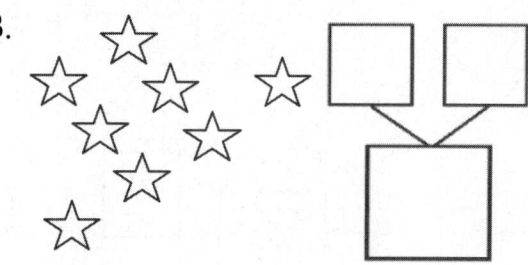

Lesson 2: Reason about embedded numbers in varied configurations using number bonds.

A STORY OF UNITS – TEKS EDITION
Lesson 2 Homework 1•1

How many animals do you see? Write at least 2 different number bonds to show different ways to break apart the total.

9.

10.

Lesson 2: Reason about embedded numbers in varied configurations using number bonds.

A STORY OF UNITS – TEKS EDITION Lesson 3 Homework Helper 1•1

Draw one more in the 5-group. In the box, write the numbers to describe the new picture.

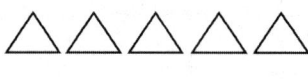
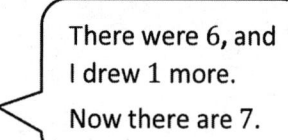

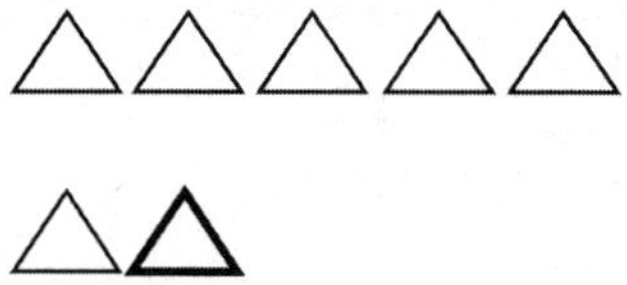

There were 6, and I drew 1 more. Now there are 7.

1 more than 6 is __7__.

6 + 1 = __7__

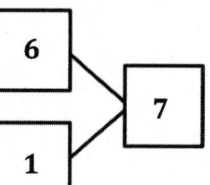

Lesson 3: See and describe numbers of objects using *1 more* within 5-group configurations.

A STORY OF UNITS – TEKS EDITION   Lesson 3 Homework 1•1

Name _____   Date _____

How many objects do you see? Draw one more. How many objects are there now?

1.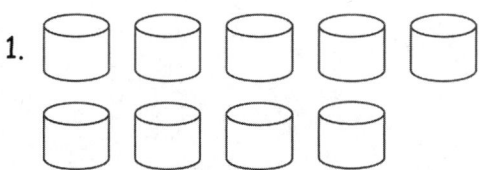

1 more than 9 is ____.

9 + 1 = ____

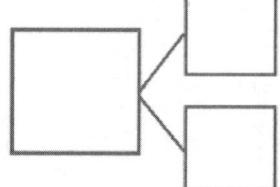

2.

____ is 1 more than 7.

____ = 7 + 1

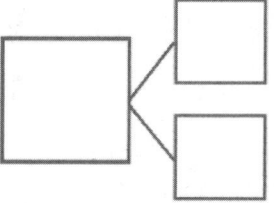

3. △ △ △ △ △

____ is 1 more than 5.

____ = 5 + 1

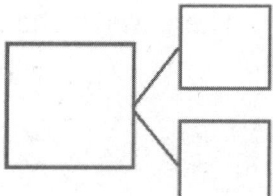

4.

1 more than 8 is ____.

____ + 1 = ____

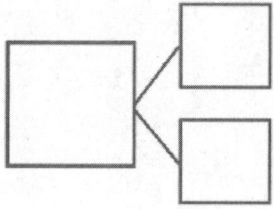

Lesson 3:   See and describe numbers of objects using *1 more* within 5-group configurations.

11

5. Imagine adding 1 more pencil to the picture.
   Then, write the numbers to match how many pencils there will be.

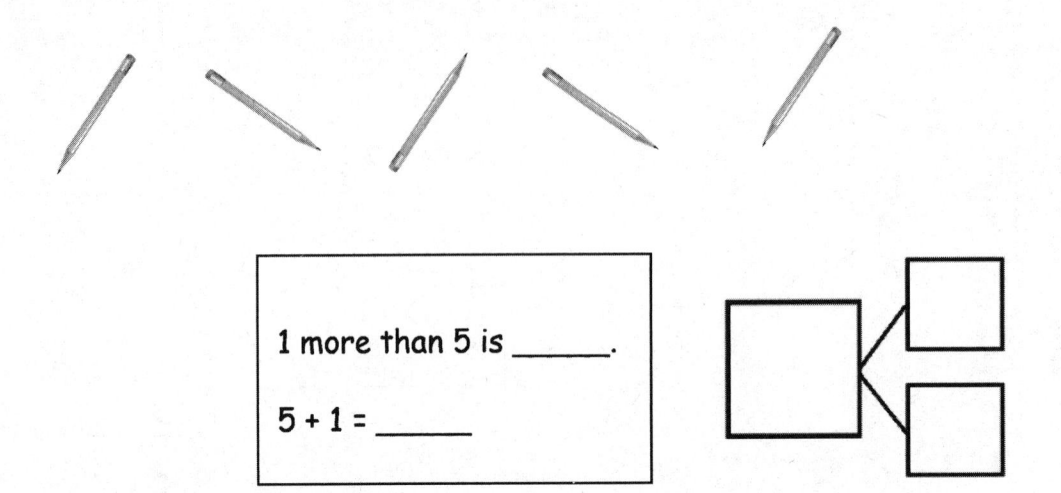

   1 more than 5 is _____.

   5 + 1 = _____

6. Imagine adding 1 more flower to the picture.
   Then, write the numbers to match how many flowers there will be.

   _____ is 1 more than 8.

   _____ + 1 = _____

A STORY OF UNITS – TEKS EDITION
Lesson 4 Homework Helper 1•1

By the end of first grade, students should know all their addition and subtraction facts within 10.

The homework for Lesson 4 provides an opportunity for students to create flashcards that will help them build fluency with all the ways to make 6 (6 and 0, 5 and 1, 4 and 2, 3 and 3).

- Some of the flashcards may have the full number bond and number sentence.

Front: Number Sentence

$2 + 4 = 6$

In this number sentence, the parts are 2 and 4. The total is 6.

Back: Number Bond

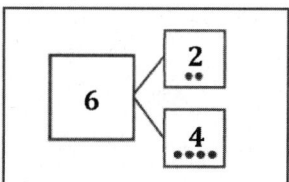

- Others may have the number bond and just the expression.

Front: Expression

$2 + 4$

2 + 4? Hmmmm... Twoooooo, 3, 4, 5, 6. The total is 6.

Back: Number Bond

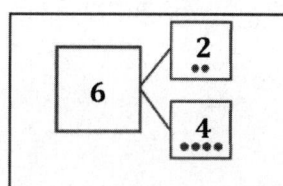

Lesson 4: Represent *put together* situations with number bonds. Count on from one embedded number or part to totals of 6 and 7, and generate all addition expressions for each total.

13

A STORY OF UNITS – TEKS EDITION

Lesson 4 Homework 1•1

Name _____ Date _____

Today, we learned the different combinations that make 6. For homework, cut out the flashcards below, and write the number sentences that you learned today on the back. Keep these flashcards in the place where you do your homework to practice ways to make 6 until you know them really well! As we continue to learn different ways to make 7, 8, 9, and 10 in the upcoming days, continue to make new flashcards.

*Note to families: Be sure students make each of the combinations that make 6. The flashcards can look something like this:

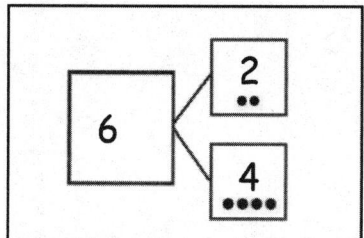

Front of Card 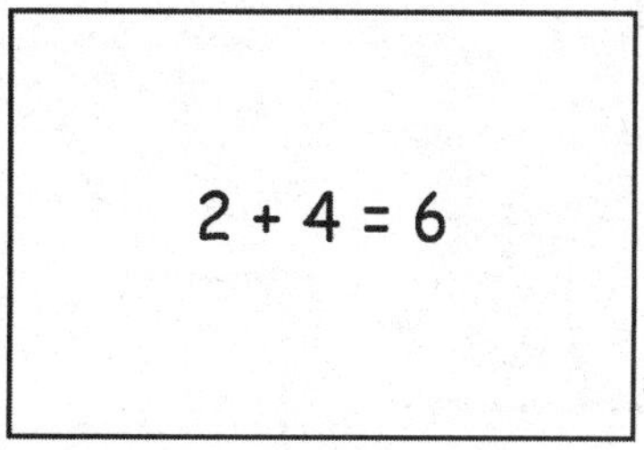   Back of Card

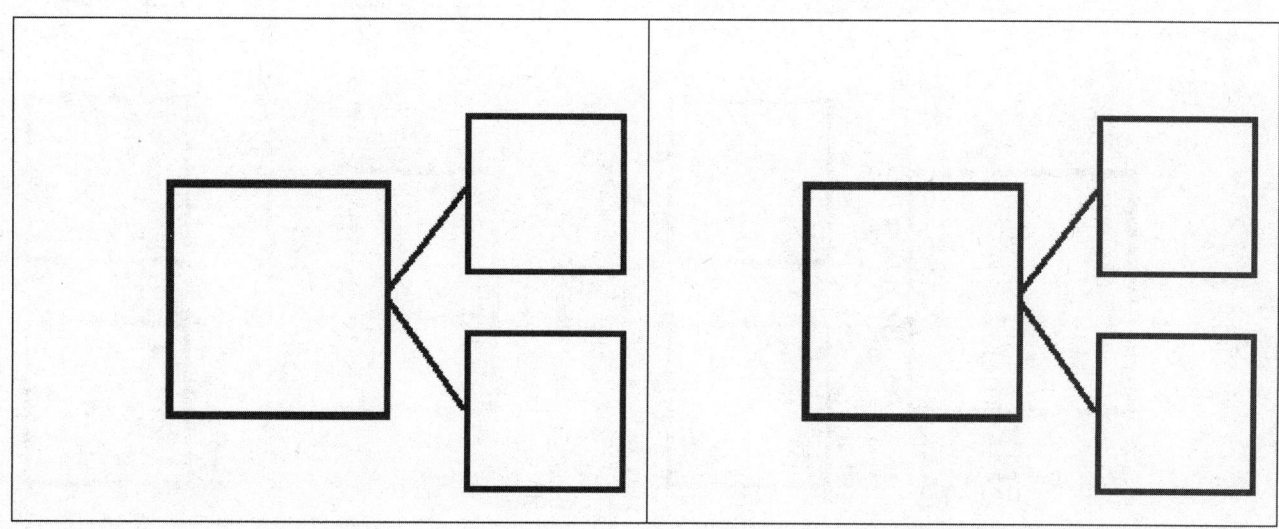

Lesson 4: Represent *put together* situations with number bonds. Count on from one embedded number or part to totals of 6 and 7, and generate all addition expressions for each total.

15

A STORY OF UNITS – TEKS EDITION

Lesson 4 Homework 1•1

Lesson 4: Represent *put together* situations with number bonds. Count on from one embedded number or part to totals of 6 and 7, and generate all addition expressions for each total.

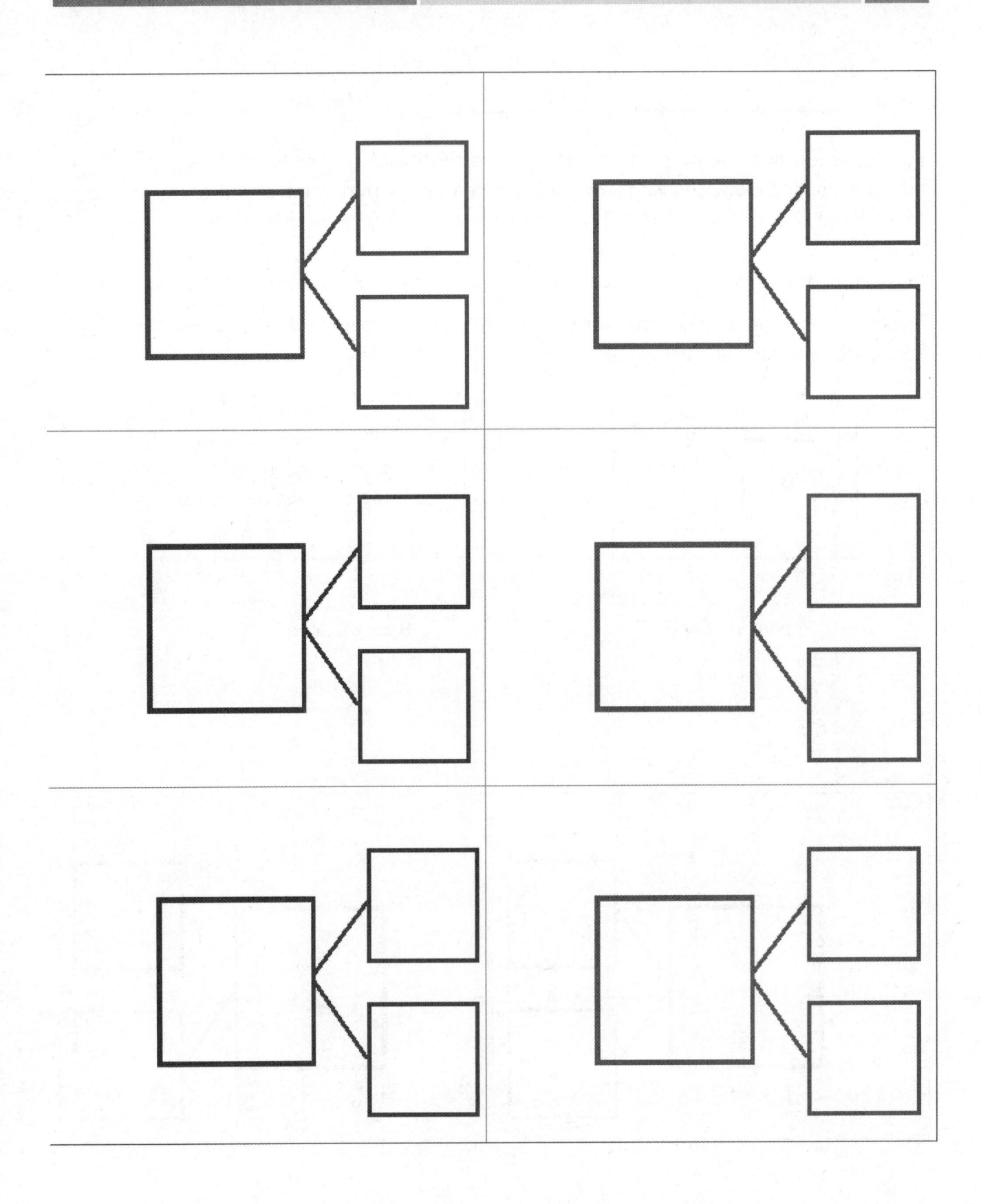

A STORY OF UNITS – TEKS EDITION   Lesson 5 Homework Helper   1•1

1. Make 2 number sentences. Use the number bonds for help.

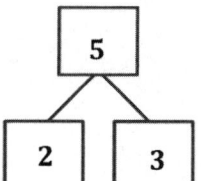

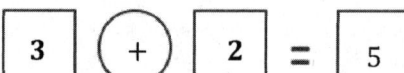

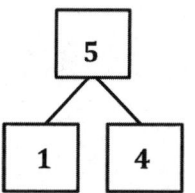

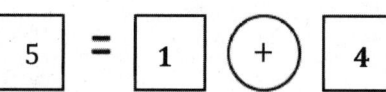

3 and 2 are the parts in one of my number bonds, so I know 3 + 2 = 5.

This number bond has the parts 1 and 4, and the whole is 5. I can write my number sentence starting with the whole, 5 = 4 + 1.

2. Fill in the missing number in the number bond. Then, write addition number sentences for the number bond you made.

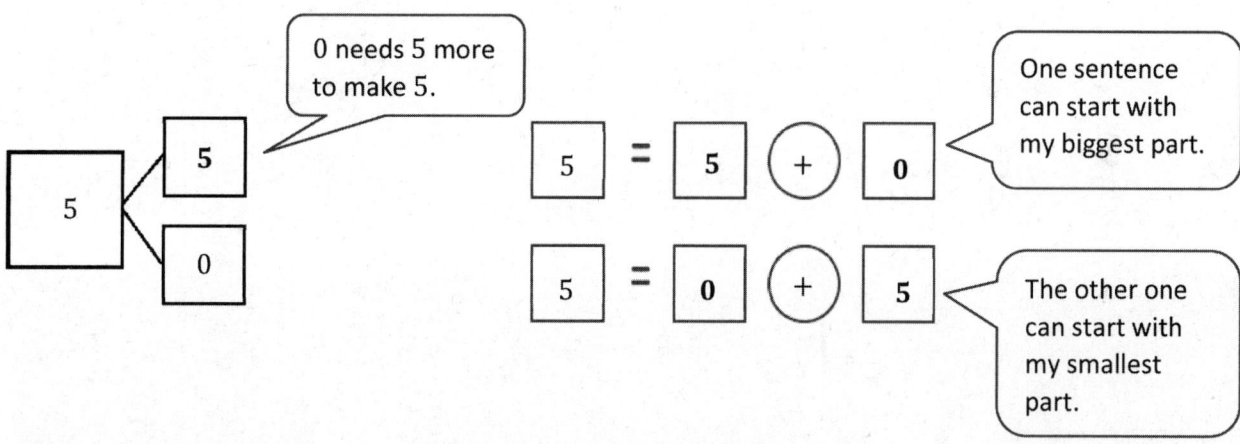

0 needs 5 more to make 5.

One sentence can start with my biggest part.

The other one can start with my smallest part.

In addition to tonight's Homework, students may wish to create flashcards that will help them build fluency with all the ways to make 7 (7 and 0, 6 and 1, 5 and 2, 4 and 3).

Lesson 5: Represent *put together* situations with number bonds. Count on from one embedded number or part to totals of 6 and 7, and generate all addition expressions for each total.

A STORY OF UNITS – TEKS EDITION

Lesson 5 Homework 1•1

Name _____ Date _____

1. Match the dice to show different ways to make 7. Then, draw a number bond for each pair of dice.

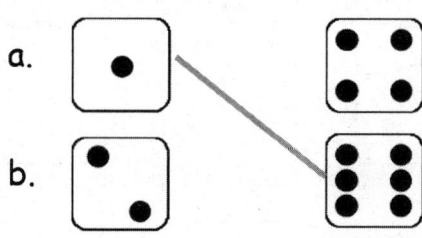
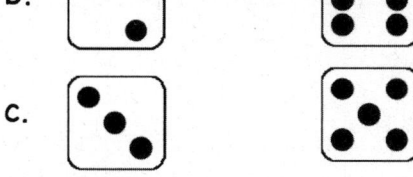

a.
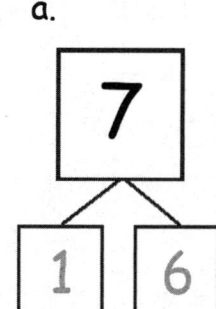

b.
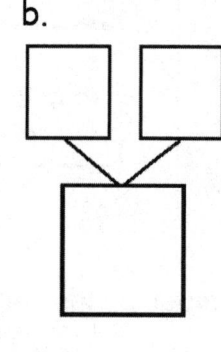

c.
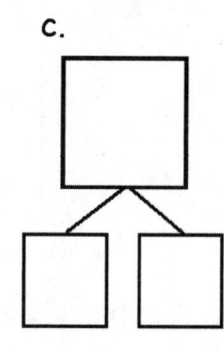

2. Make 2 number sentences. Use the number bonds above for help.

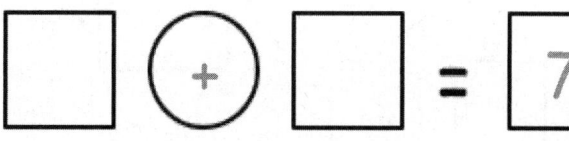

3. Fill in the missing number in the number bond. Then, write addition number sentences for the number bond you made.

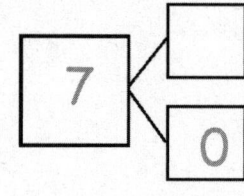

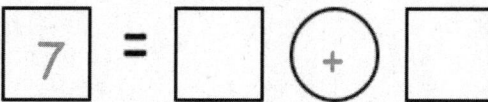

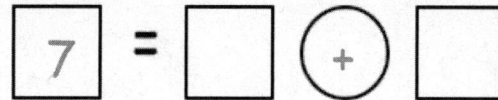

Lesson 5: Represent *put together* situations with number bonds. Count on from one embedded number or part to totals of 6 and 7, and generate all addition expressions for each total.

19

4. Color the dominoes that make 7.

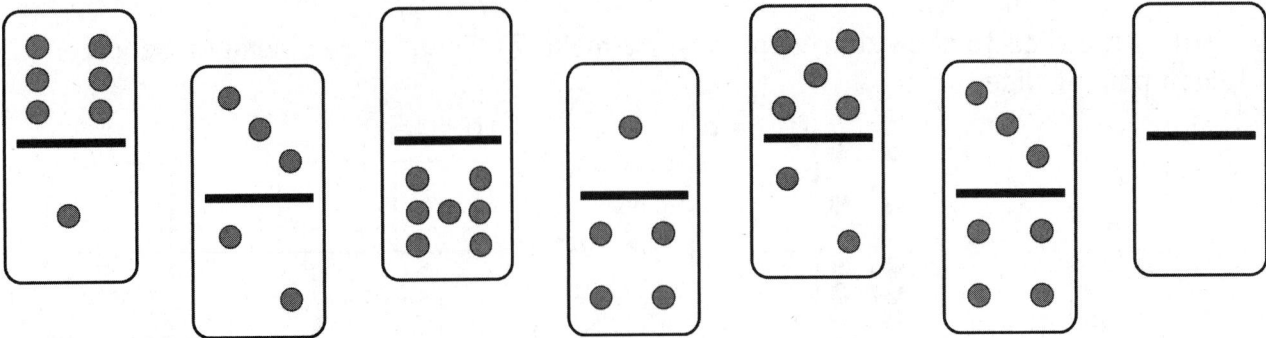

5. Complete the number bonds for the dominoes you colored.

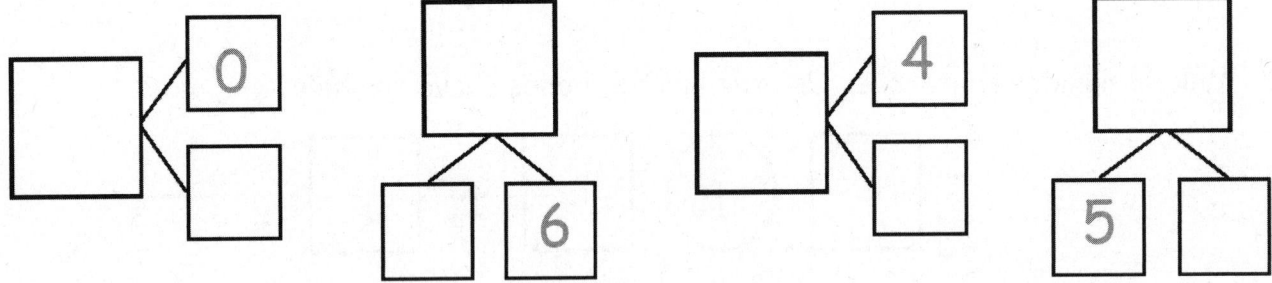

A STORY OF UNITS – TEKS EDITION   Lesson 6 Homework Helper   1•1

1. Show 2 ways to make 7. Use the number bond for help.

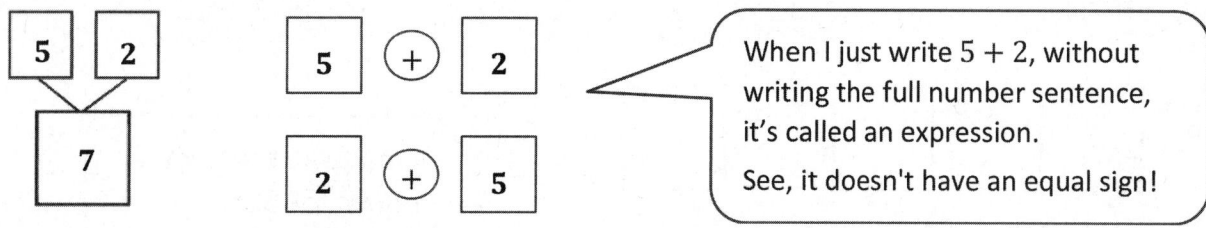

When I just write 5 + 2, without writing the full number sentence, it's called an expression.
See, it doesn't have an equal sign!

2. Fill in the missing number in the number bond. Write 2 addition sentences for the number bond.

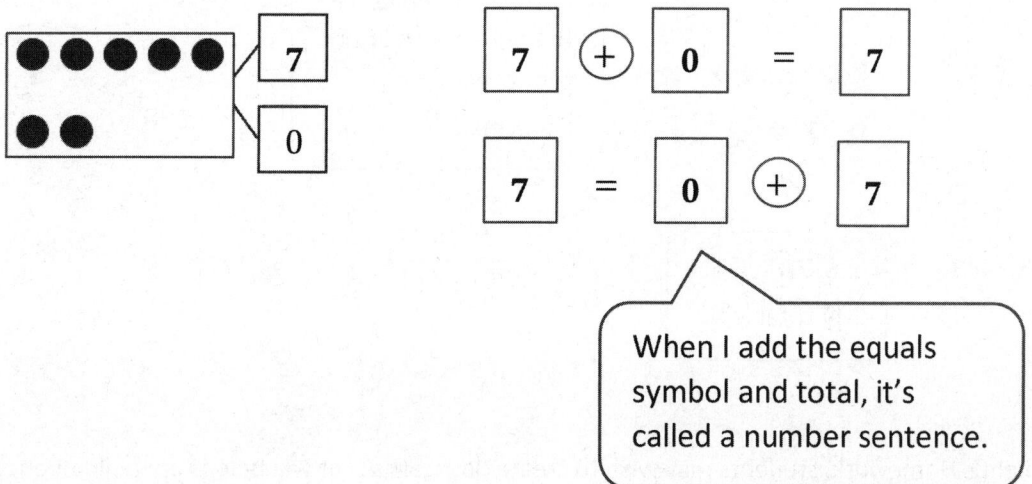

When I add the equals symbol and total, it's called a number sentence.

Lesson 6: Represent *put together* situations with number bonds. Count on from one embedded number or part to totals of 8 and 9, and generate all expressions for each total.

21

3. These number bonds are in an order, starting with the smallest part first. Write to show which number bonds are missing.

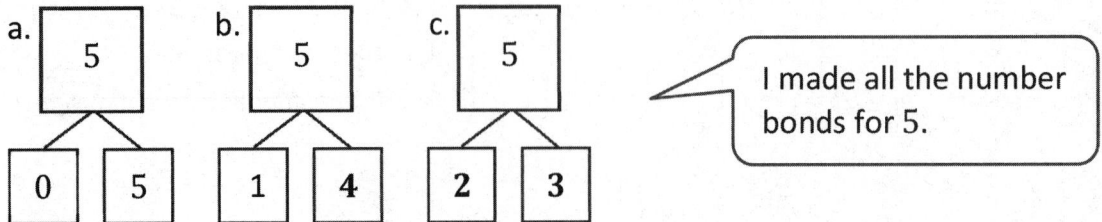

I made all the number bonds for 5.

4. Use the expression to write a number bond, and draw a picture that makes 8.

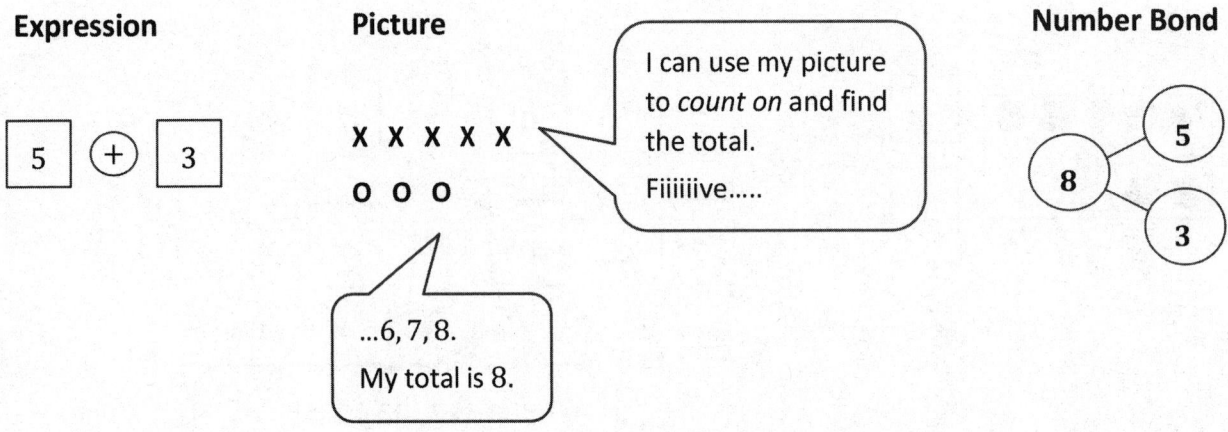

In addition to tonight's Homework, students may wish to create flashcards that will help them build fluency with all the ways to make 8 (8 and 0, 7 and 1, 6 and 2, 5 and 3, 4 and 4).

A STORY OF UNITS – TEKS EDITION   Lesson 6 Homework 1•1

Name _____   Date _____

1. Match the dots to show different ways to make 8. Then, draw a number bond for each pair.

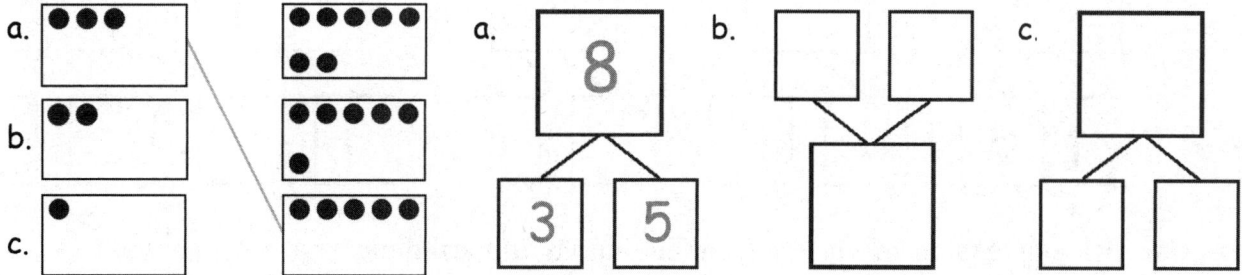

2. Show 2 ways to make 8. Use the number bonds above for help.

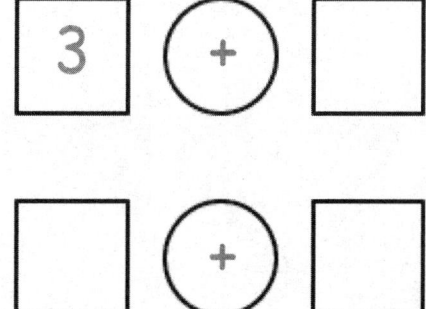

3. Fill in the missing number in the number bond. Write 2 addition sentences for the number bond you made. Notice where the equal sign is to make your sentence true.

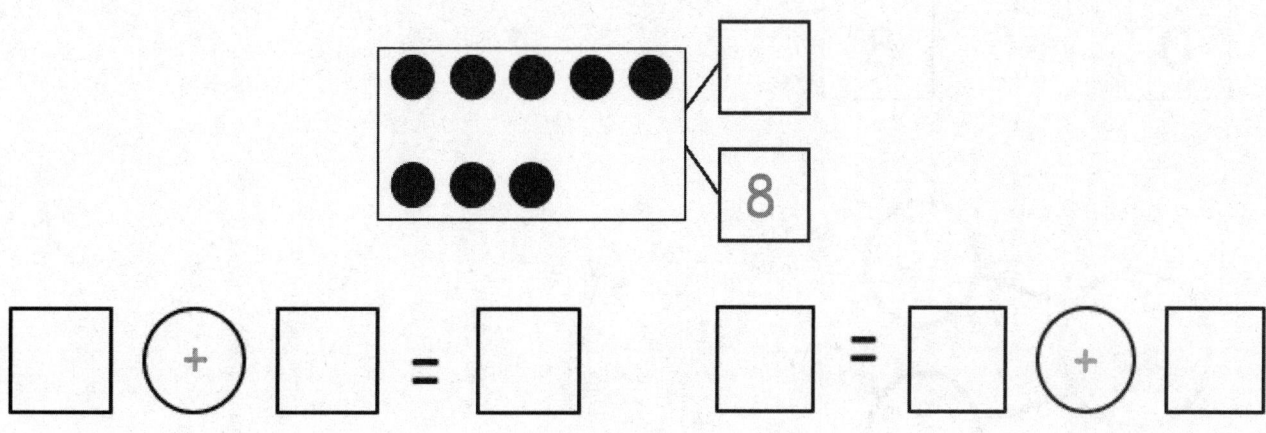

Lesson 6: Represent *put together* situations with number bonds. Count on from one embedded number or part to totals of 8 and 9, and generate all expressions for each total.

23

A STORY OF UNITS – TEKS EDITION   Lesson 6 Homework   1•1

4. These number bonds are in an order starting with the smallest part first. Write to show which number bonds are missing.

a. 8 / 0 8   b. 8 / 1 ☐   c. 8 / ☐ 6   d. 8 / 3 ☐   e. 8 / ☐ ☐

5. Use the expression to write a number bond and draw a picture that makes 8.

2 + 6

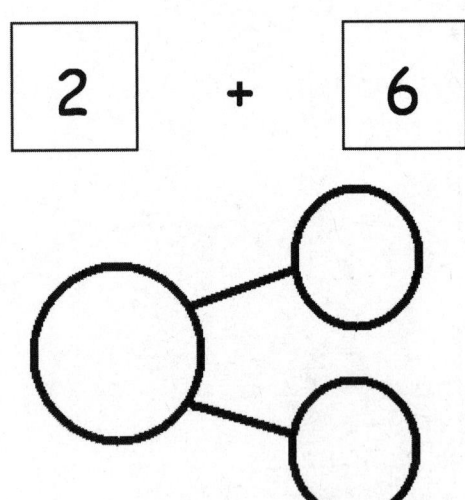

6. Use the expression to write a number bond and draw a picture that makes 8.

0 + 8

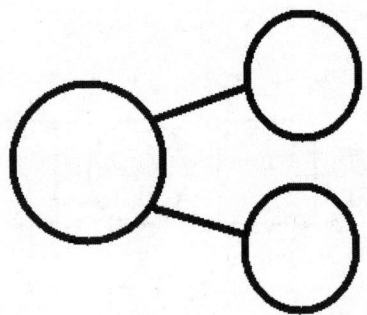

Lesson 6: Represent *put together* situations with number bonds. Count on from one embedded number or part to totals of 8 and 9, and generate all expressions for each total.

A STORY OF UNITS – TEKS EDITION

Lesson 7 Homework Helper 1•1

Use the pond picture to help you write the expressions and number bonds to show all of the different ways to make 8.

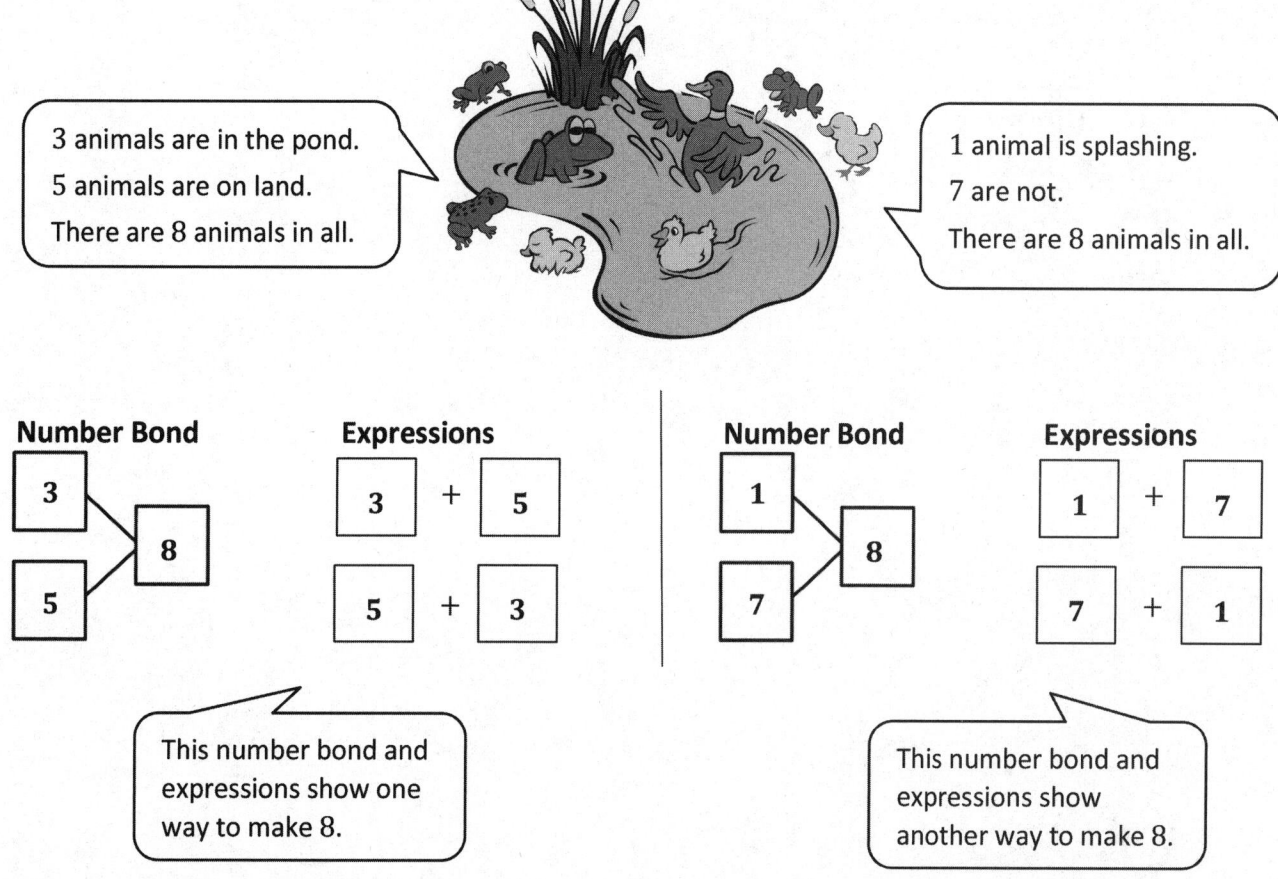

3 animals are in the pond.
5 animals are on land.
There are 8 animals in all.

1 animal is splashing.
7 are not.
There are 8 animals in all.

Number Bond 3, 5 → 8

Expressions
3 + 5
5 + 3

This number bond and expressions show one way to make 8.

Number Bond 1, 7 → 8

Expressions
1 + 7
7 + 1

This number bond and expressions show another way to make 8.

In addition to tonight's Homework, students may wish to create flashcards that will help them build fluency with all the ways to make 9 (9 and 0, 8 and 1, 7 and 2, 6 and 3, 5 and 4).

Lesson 7: Represent *put together* situations with number bonds. Count on from one embedded number or part to totals of 8 and 9, and generate all expressions for each total.

A STORY OF UNITS – TEKS EDITION Lesson 7 Homework 1•1

Name _____   Date _____

Ways to Make 9

Use the bookshelf picture to help you write the expressions and number bonds to show all of the different ways to make 9.

Lesson 7: Represent put together situations with number bonds. Count on from one embedded number or part to totals of 8 and 9, and generate all expressions for each total.

27

A STORY OF UNITS – TEKS EDITION

Lesson 7 Template 1   1•1

9 books picture card

Lesson 7: Represent put together situations with number bonds. Count on from one embedded number or part to totals of 8 and 9, and generate all expressions for each total.

A STORY OF UNITS – TEKS EDITION Lesson 8 Homework Helper 1•1

1. Rex found 10 bones on his walk. He can't decide which part he wants to bring to his doghouse and which part he should bury. Help show Rex his choices by filling in the missing parts of the number bonds.

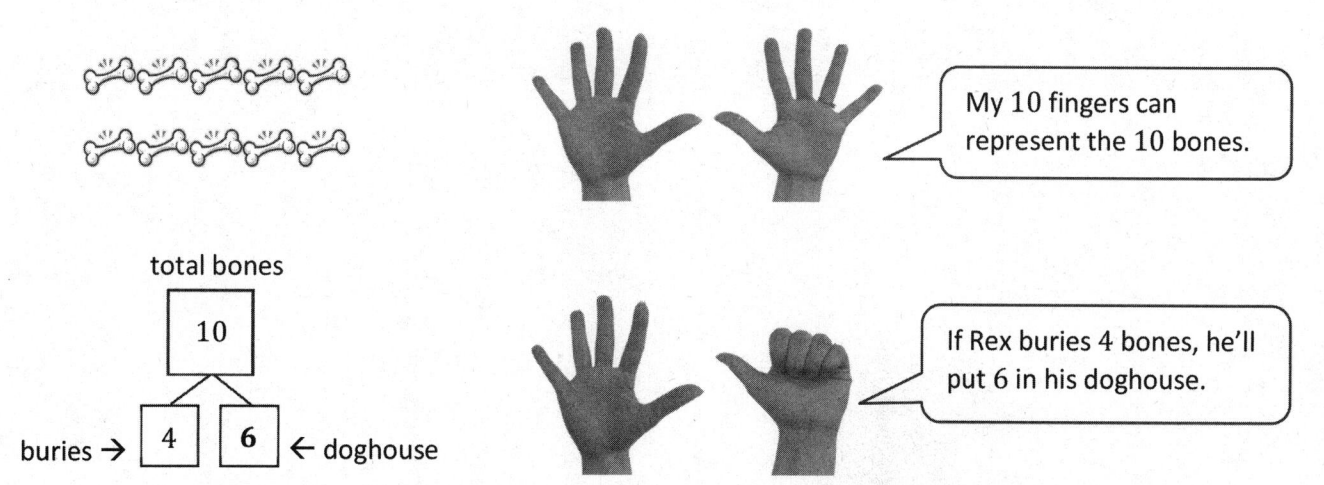

   total bones: 10
   buries → 4   6 ← doghouse

   My 10 fingers can represent the 10 bones.

   If Rex buries 4 bones, he'll put 6 in his doghouse.

2. Write all the adding sentences that match this number bond.

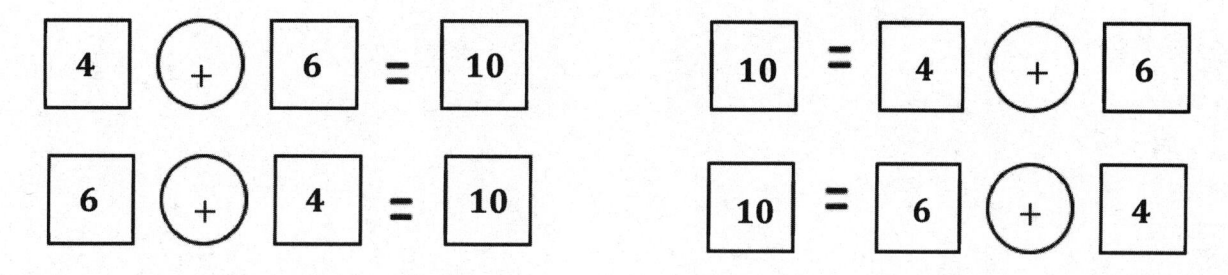

   4 + 6 = 10   10 = 4 + 6
   6 + 4 = 10   10 = 6 + 4

In addition to tonight's Homework, students may wish to create flashcards that will help them build fluency with all the ways to make 10 (10 and 0, 9 and 1, 8 and 2, 7 and 3, 6 and 4, 5 and 5).

Lesson 8: Represent all the number pairs of 10 as number bonds from a given scenario, and generate all expressions equal to 10.

A STORY OF UNITS – TEKS EDITION

Lesson 8 Homework 1•1

Name _____ Date _____

1. Rex found 10 bones on his walk. He can't decide which part he wants to bring to his doghouse and which part he should bury. Help show Rex his choices by filling in the missing parts of the number bonds.

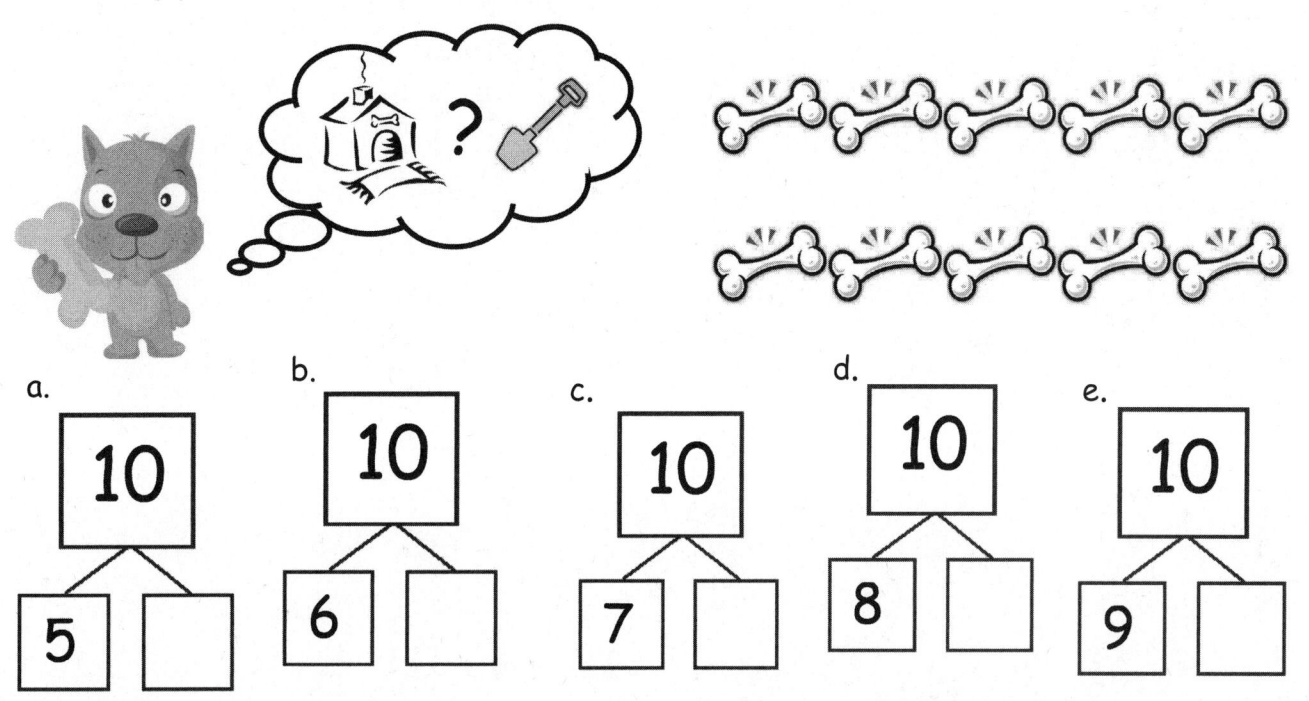

a. 10 / 5, ☐
b. 10 / 6, ☐
c. 10 / 7, ☐
d. 10 / 8, ☐
e. 10 / 9, ☐

2. He decided to bury 3 and bring 7 back home. Write all the adding sentences that match this number bond.

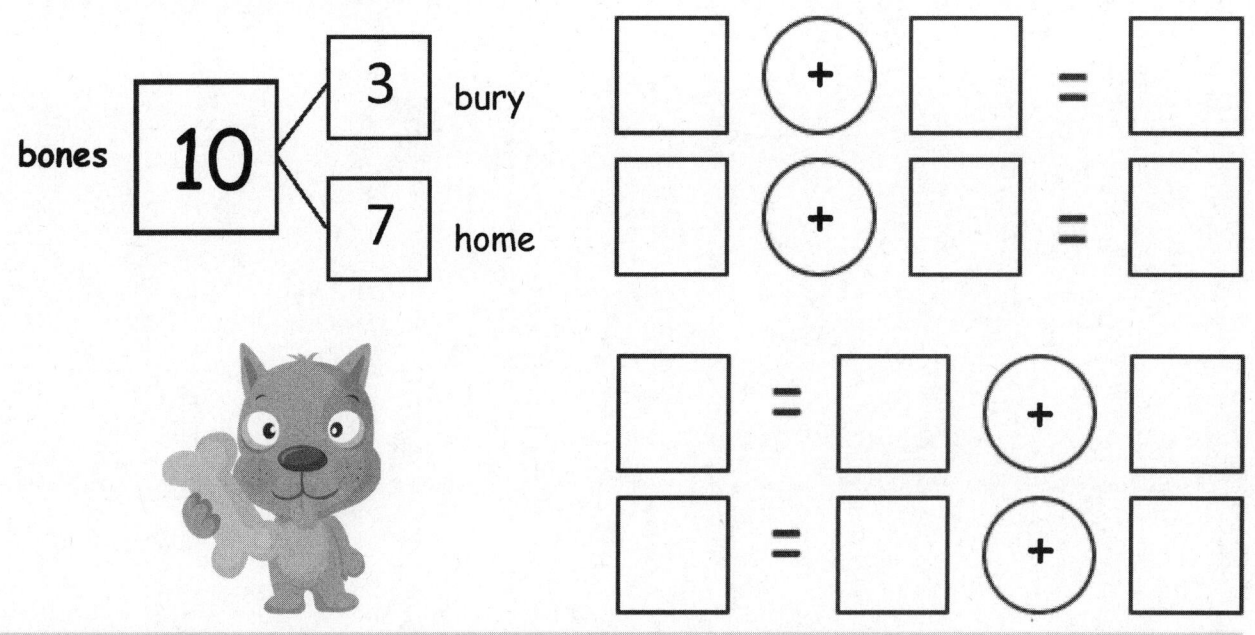

bones 10 — 3 bury
         — 7 home

☐ + ☐ = ☐

☐ + ☐ = ☐

☐ = ☐ + ☐

☐ = ☐ + ☐

Lesson 8: Represent all the number pairs of 10 as number bonds from a given scenario, and generate all expressions equal to 10.

33

A STORY OF UNITS – TEKS EDITION

Lesson 9 Homework Helper 1•1

1. a. Use the picture to tell a math story.

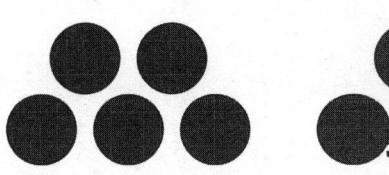

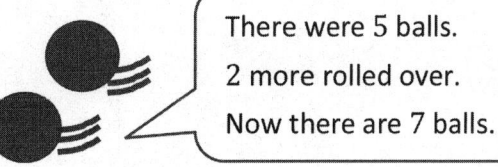

There were 5 balls.
2 more rolled over.
Now there are 7 balls.

b. Write a number bond to match your story.

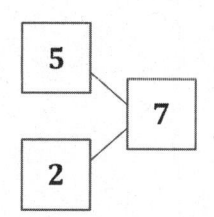

5
2
7

c. Write a number sentence to tell the story.

5 + 2 = 7

d. There are __7__ balls.

2. Marcus has 5 red blocks and 3 yellow blocks. How many blocks does Marcus have?

red

yellow

5
3
8

I can draw a math picture and number bond to match the story!

5 + 3 = 8

Marcus has __8__ blocks.

Then I can answer the question with a number sentence and word sentence.

Lesson 9: Solve *add to with result unknown* and *put together with result unknown* math stories by drawing, writing equations, and making statements of the solution.

35

A STORY OF UNITS – TEKS EDITION   Lesson 9 Homework 1•1

Name _____   Date _____

1. Use the picture to tell a math story.

Write a number bond to match your story.

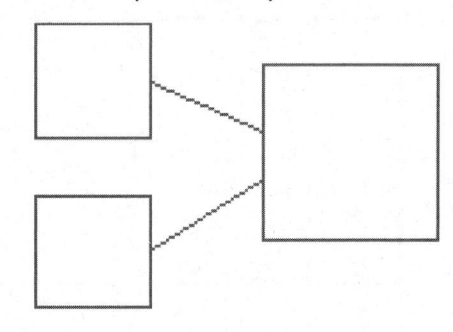

Write a number sentence to tell the story.

There are ____ sharks.

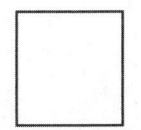

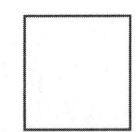

☐ + ☐ = ☐

2. Use the picture to tell a math story.

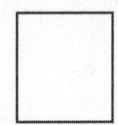

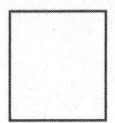

Write a number bond to match your story.

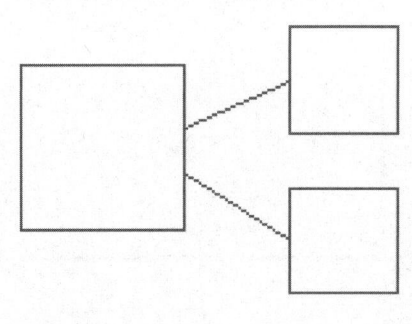

Write a number sentence to tell the story.

There are ____ students.

☐ = ☐ + ☐

Lesson 9: Solve *add to with result unknown* and *put together with result unknown* math stories by drawing, writing equations, and making statements of the solution.

37

Draw a picture to match the story.

3. Jim has 4 big dogs and 3 small dogs. How many dogs does Jim have?

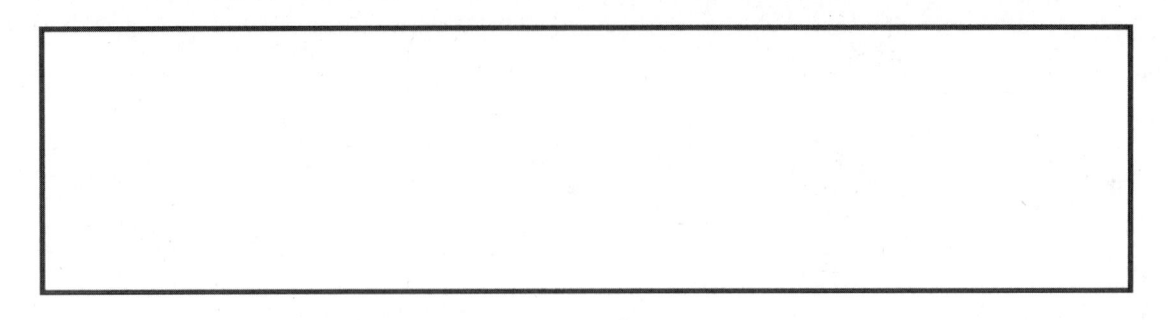

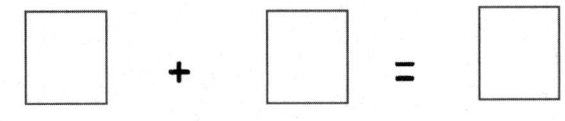

☐ + ☐ = ☐   Jim has ____ dogs.

4. Liv plays at the park. She plays with 3 girls and 6 boys. How many kids does she play with at the park?

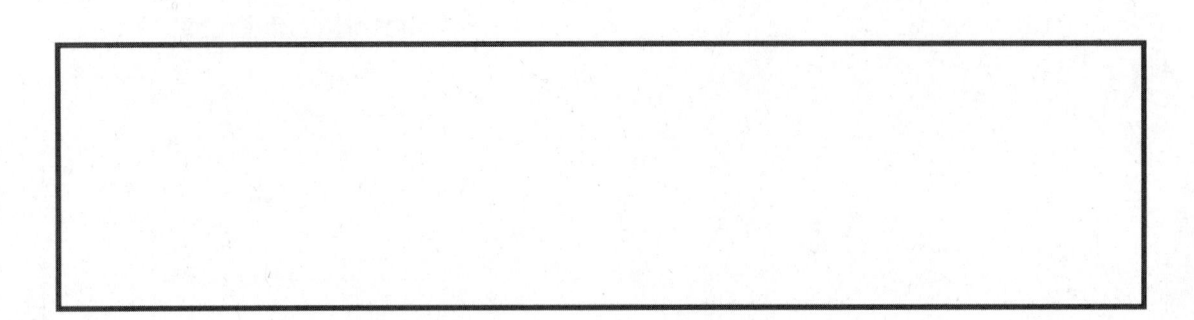

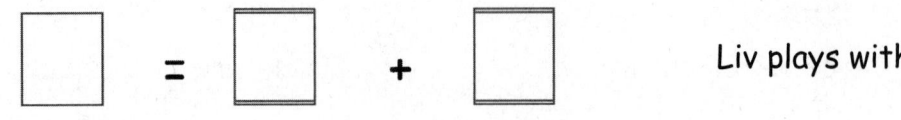

☐ = ☐ + ☐   Liv plays with ____ kids.

A STORY OF UNITS – TEKS EDITION　　　Lesson 10 Homework Helper　1•1

1. a. Use your 5-group cards to solve.

   b. Draw the other 5-group card to show what you did.

   I see 4 little tortoises and 3 big tortoises.

   | 4 | o o o |

   My 5-group cards can help me add. I just start at 4 and count on 3 more. Foooour..., 5, 6, 7.

   $4 + 3 = 7$

   My number sentence shows that 4 little tortoises plus 3 big tortoises equals 7 total tortoises.

2. Kira has 3 cats and 4 dogs. Draw a picture to show how many pets she has.

   cats　　　**dogs**
   ○○○　　○○○○

   My math picture can be just circles!

   $3 + 4 = 7$

   Number bond: parts 4 and 3, total 7.

   My number sentence shows that 3 cats plus 4 dogs equals 7 pets!

   In my number bond, the parts are 4 and 3. The total is 7.

   Kira has __7__ pets.

Lesson 10: Solve *put together with result unknown* math stories by drawing and using 5-group cards.

39

A STORY OF UNITS – TEKS EDITION

Lesson 10 Homework 1•1

Name _____ Date _____

1. Use your 5-group cards to solve.

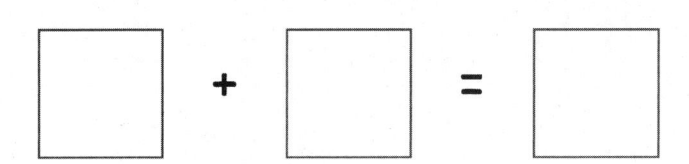

   ☐ + ☐ = ☐

   Draw the other 5-group card to show what you did.

   | 5 | ☐ |

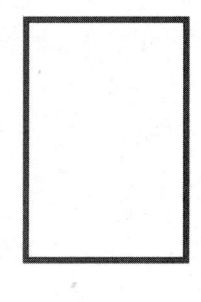

2. Use your 5-group cards to solve.

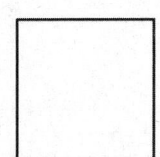

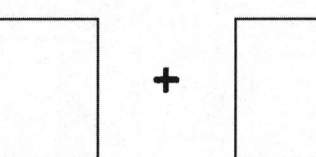

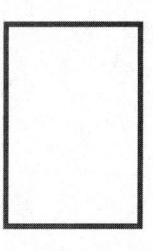

   ☐ = ☐ + ☐

   Draw the other 5-group card to show what you did.

   | 4 | ☐ |

Lesson 10: Solve *put together with result unknown* math stories by drawing and using 5-group cards.

41

A STORY OF UNITS – TEKS EDITION   Lesson 10 Homework   1•1

3. There are 4 tall boys and 5 short boys. Draw to show how many boys there are in all.

There are _____ boys in all.

Write a number sentence to show what you did.

☐ + ☐ = ☐

Write a number bond to match the story.

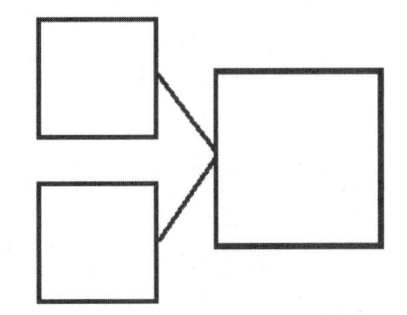

4. There are 3 girls and 5 boys. Draw to show how many children there are altogether.

There are _____ children altogether.

Write a number sentence to show what you did.

☐ + ☐ = ☐

Write a number bond to match the story.

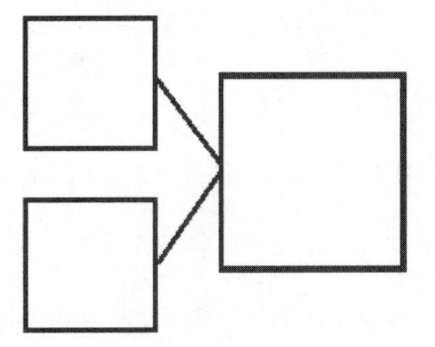

Lesson 10: Solve *put together with result unknown* math stories by drawing and using 5-group cards.

A STORY OF UNITS – TEKS EDITION

Lesson 10 Template 1 1•1

0	1	2	3
4	5	<u>6</u>	7
8	<u>9</u>	10	10
	10	5	5

5-group cards - from Lesson 5

Lesson 10: Solve *put together with result unknown* math stories by drawing and using 5-group cards.

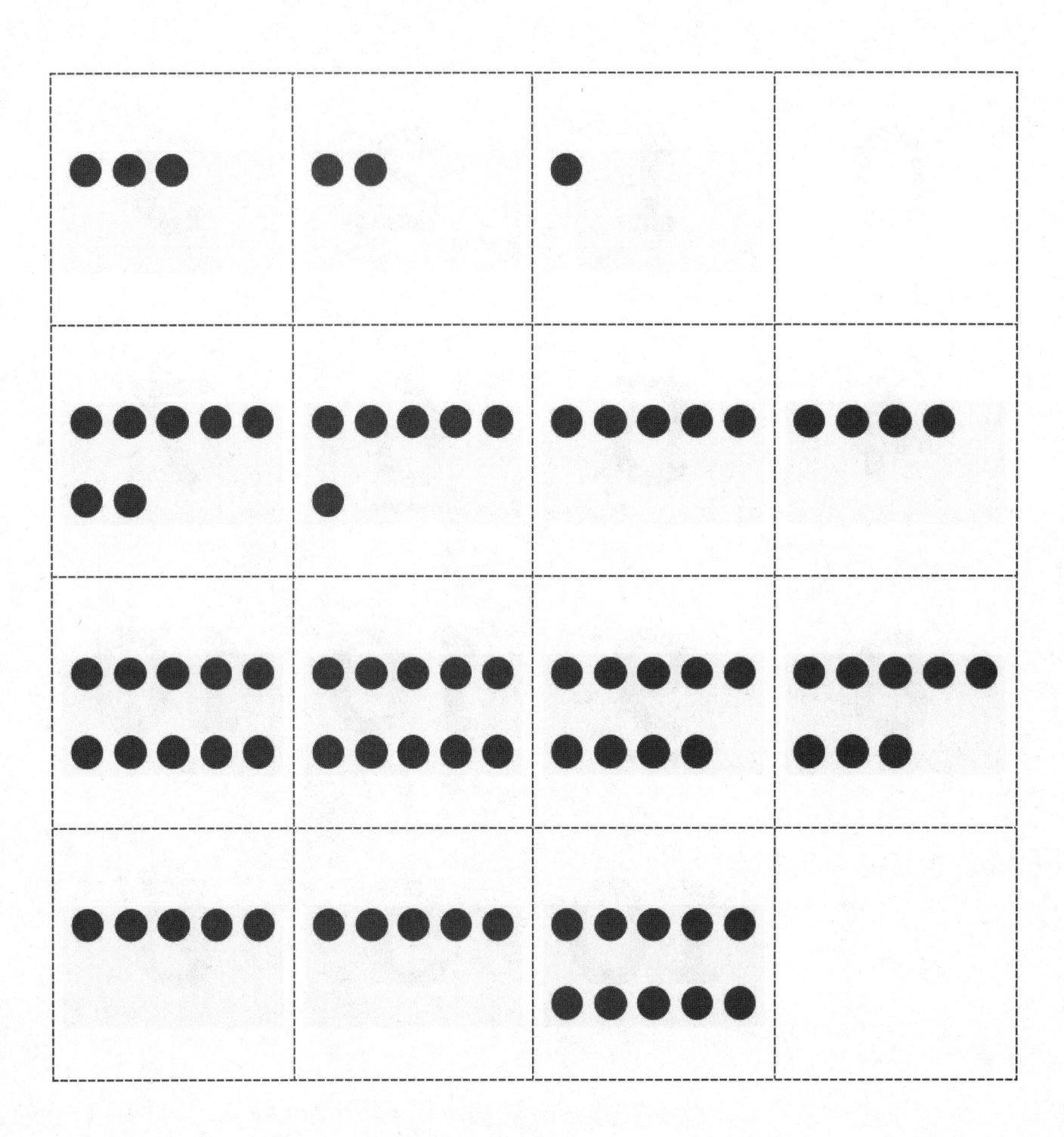

A STORY OF UNITS – TEKS EDITION

Lesson 10 Template 1   1•1

5-group cards, dot side - from Lesson 5

Lesson 10: Solve *put together with result unknown* math stories by drawing and using 5-group cards.

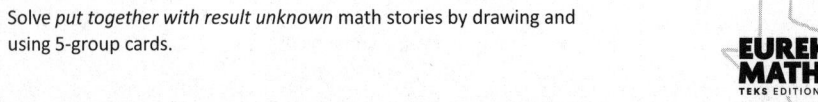

A STORY OF UNITS – TEKS EDITION
Lesson 11 Homework Helper 1•1

1. Use the 5-group cards to count on to find the missing number in the number sentences.

   5 + ? = 8   5 + 3 = 8

   > 5 plus "the mystery number" equals 8. Hmmm…..

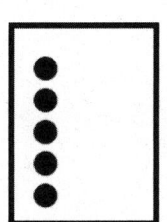

   > I can draw dots as I *count on* to 8. Fiiiiive…, 6, 7, 8.

   > I drew 3 more dots. "The mystery number" is 3.

2. Match the number sentence to the math story. Draw a picture, or use your 5-group cards to solve.

   Larry had 3 books. His brother gave him some more. Now he has 9 books. How many books did Larry's brother give him?

   had   **brother**

   ooo | oooooo

   Larry's brother gave him __6__ books.

   4 + ? = 7

   3 + ? = 9

   > I can draw 3 circles to show how many books Larry had. Then I can draw more until there are 9.

   > I drew 6 more circles, so his brother must have given him 6 books.

   > This number sentence matches the story because 3 books plus "the mystery number" of books equals 9 total books.

Lesson 11: Solve add to with change unknown math stories as a context for counting on by drawing, writing equations, and making statements of the solution.

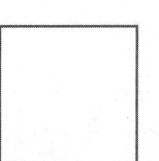

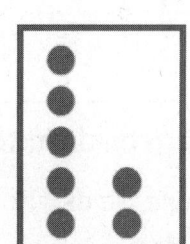

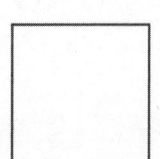

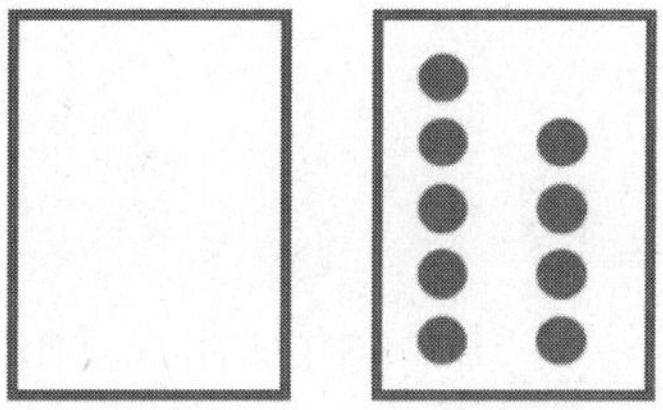

Name _____ Date _____

1. Use the 5-group cards to count on to find the missing number in the number sentences.

a. $2 + \boxed{} = 7$

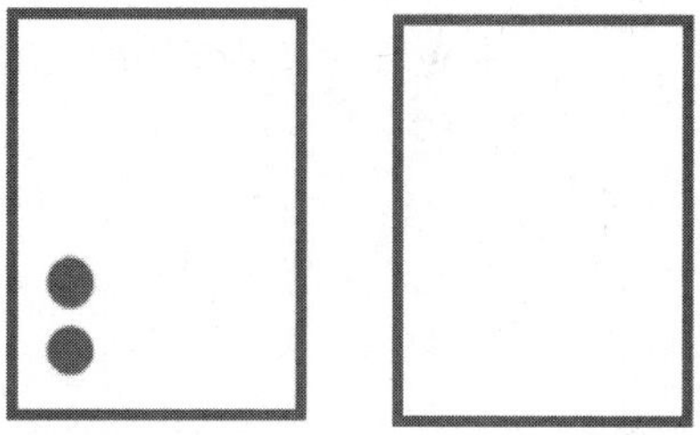

b. $8 = 5 + \boxed{}$

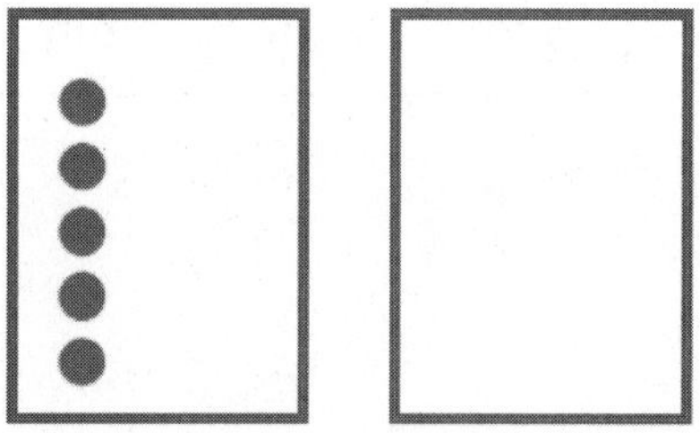

c. $9 = 7 + \boxed{}$

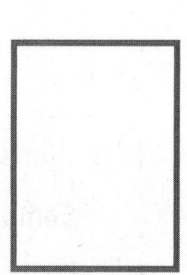

d. $9 = \boxed{} + 9$

A STORY OF UNITS – TEKS EDITION   Lesson 11 Homework   1•1

2. Match the number sentence to the math story. Draw a picture or use your 5-group cards to solve.

a. Scott has 3 cookies. His mom gives him some more. Now, he has 8 cookies. How many cookies did his mom give him?

   Scott's mom gave him _____ cookies.

   [6] + [?] = [9]

   [3] + [?] = [8]

b. Kim sees 6 birds in the tree.
   Some more birds fly in.
   Kim sees 9 birds in the tree. How many birds flew to the tree?

   _____ birds flew to the tree.

   [4] + [?] = [8]

48   Lesson 11:   Solve add to with change unknown math stories as a context for counting on by drawing, writing equations, and making statements of the solution.

A STORY OF UNITS – TEKS EDITION   Lesson 12 Homework Helper   1•1

1. Use your 5-group cards to count on to find the missing number in the number sentences.

   $5 + ? = 9$

   The mystery number is 4.

   > I can *count on* from 5 to find the mystery number.
   > Fiiiiiive..., 6, 7, 8, 9.
   > I counted on 4 more, so the mystery number is 4.

2. Shana had 5 hats. Then she bought some more. She has 8 hats now. How many hats did she buy?

   > 5 plus "the mystery number" equals 8.
   > Hmmm...

   > I can start at 5 and draw dots as I *count on* to 8.
   > Fiiiiive..., 6, 7, 8.

   $5 + 3 = 8$

   > I drew 3 more dots. The "mystery number" is 3.

   Shana bought __3__ hats.

   Lesson 12: Solve *add to with change unknown* math stories using 5-group cards.

A STORY OF UNITS – TEKS EDITION

Lesson 12 Homework 1•1

Name _____ Date _____

Use your 5-group cards to count on to find the missing number in the number sentences.

1. 5 + ? = 7

The mystery number is ☐

2. 2 + ? = 8

The mystery number is ☐

3. 6 + ? = 9

The mystery number is ☐

Lesson 12: Solve *add to with change unknown* math stories using 5-group cards.

51

A STORY OF UNITS – TEKS EDITION

Lesson 12 Homework 1•1

Use your 5-group cards to count on and solve the math stories. Use the boxes to show your 5-group cards.

4. Jack reads 4 books on Monday. He reads some more on Tuesday. He reads 7 books total. How many books does Jack read on Tuesday?

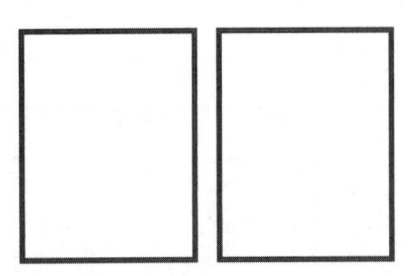

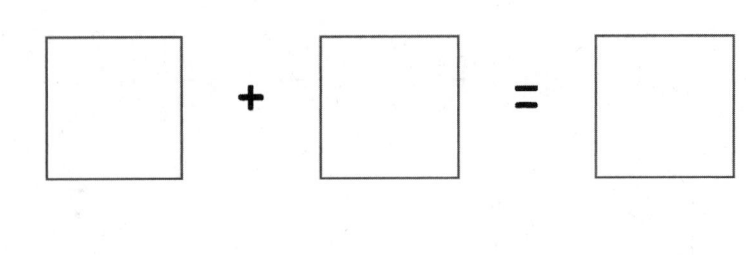

☐ + ☐ = ☐

Jack reads ____ books on Tuesday.

5. Kate has 1 sister and some brothers. She has 7 brothers and sisters in all. How many brothers does Kate have?

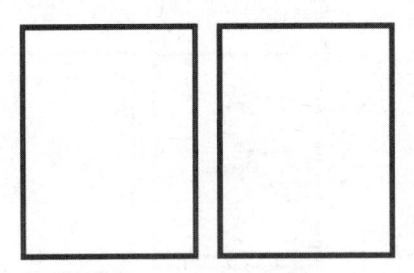

☐ + ☐ = ☐

Kate has ____ brothers.

6. There are 6 dogs in the park and some cats. There are 9 dogs and cats in the park altogether. How many cats are in the park?

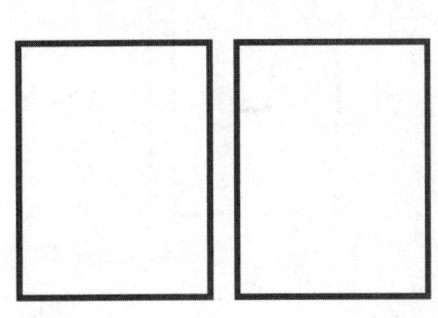

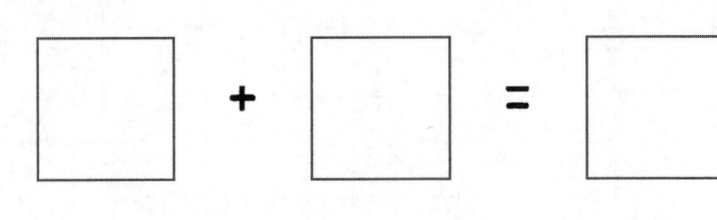

☐ + ☐ = ☐

There are ____ cats total.

Lesson 12: Solve *add to with change unknown* math stories using 5-group cards.

A STORY OF UNITS – TEKS EDITION

Lesson 13 Homework Helper 1•1

Use the number sentences to draw a picture, and then fill in the number bond to tell a math story.

1. $3 + 3 = 6$

> Hmmm... What story could I tell to match the number sentence $3 + 3 = 6$?

> I have an idea! I baked 3 round cookies and 3 heart-shaped cookies. I baked 6 cookies in total. I can draw the cookies to show my story.

> I can make a number bond to match my story!

Number bond: 3 and 3 make 6.

2. $4 + ? = 6$

> Hmmm... this problem has a mystery number.
> I know a story that would match! My brother had 4 marbles. Then he found some marbles under the couch. Now he has 6 marbles. How many marbles did he find?

> I can draw 4 circles for the marbles he had. Then I can draw some more circles until I have 6 marbles.

Number bond: 4 and 2 make 6.

Lesson 13: Tell *put together with result unknown, add to with result unknown, and add to with change unknown* stories from equations.

53

A STORY OF UNITS – TEKS EDITION

Lesson 13 Homework 1•1

Name _____ Date _____

Use the number sentences to draw a picture, and fill in the number bond to tell a math story.

1. 5 + 2 = 7

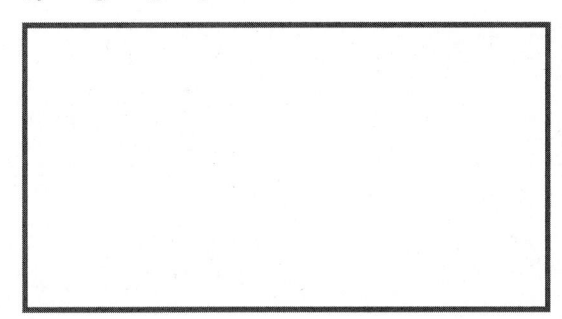

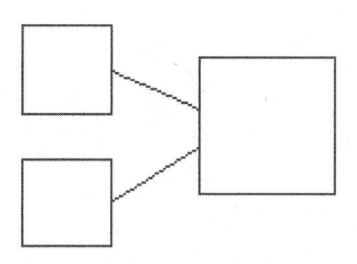

2. 3 + 6 = 9

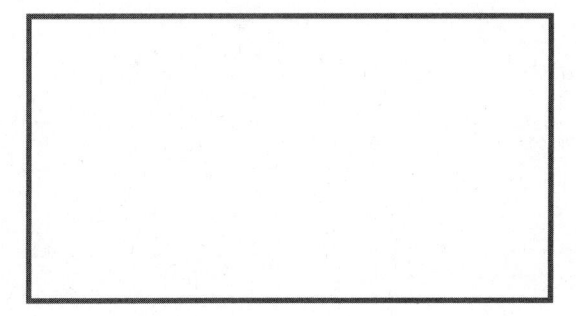

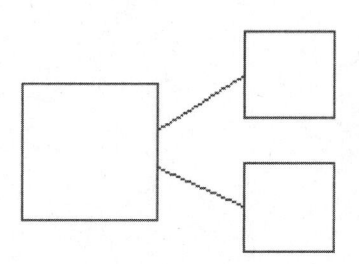

3. 7 + ? = 9

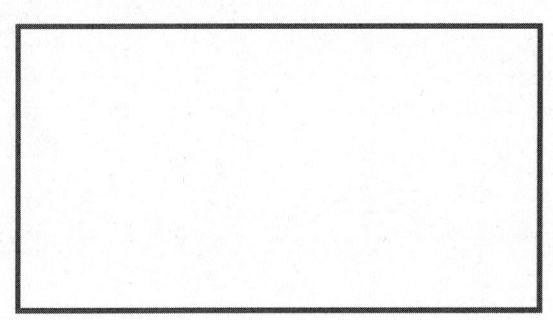

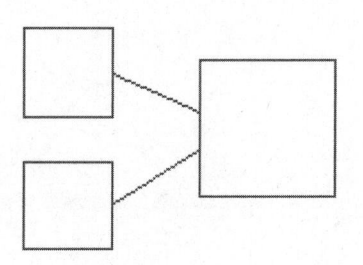

Lesson 13: Tell *put together with result unknown, add to with result unknown, and add to with change unknown* stories from equations.

A STORY OF UNITS – TEKS EDITION

Lesson 14 Homework Helper 1•1

Count on to add.

To add 6 + 2, I don't have to count all my fingers. I can just start at 6 and *count on* 2 fingers!

Siiiiix...

..., 7, 8

Write what you say when you count on.

6, ... 7, 8

a. 6 + 2 = 8

There are 2 missing numbers for this problem. I can make up my own *count on* problem!

Fiiiive...

...6, 7, 8.

5, ... 6, 7, 8

b. 8 = 5 + 3

Lesson 14: Count on up to 3 more using numeral and 5-group cards and fingers to track the change.

57

Lesson 14 Homework 1•1

Name _____ Date _____

Count on to add.

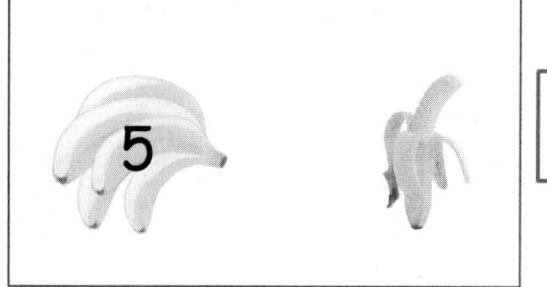

a. 5 + 1 = ☐   *(thought: 5, 6)*

Write what you say when you count on.

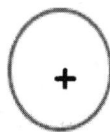

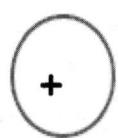

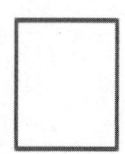

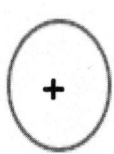

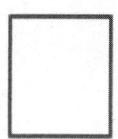

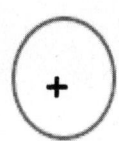

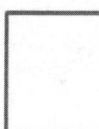

b. 5 + 2 = ☐

c. 7 + 2 = ☐

d. ☐ = 6 + 3

e. ☐ = 7 + ☐

A STORY OF UNITS – TEKS EDITION

Lesson 15 Homework Helper

1•1

Use your 5-group cards or your fingers to count on to solve.

1.

5 + 2 = 7

I'll start at 5 and *count on* 2 fingers. Fiiiive...

...6, 7.

Show the shortcut you used to add.

5 + 2 = 7

I used my fingers as a shortcut, so I'll draw them!

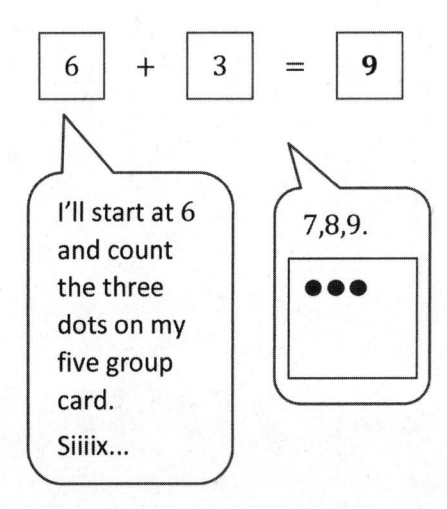

2.

6 + 3 = 9

I'll start at 6 and count the three dots on my five group card. Siiiix...

7, 8, 9.

Show the shortcut you used to add.

6 + 3 = 9

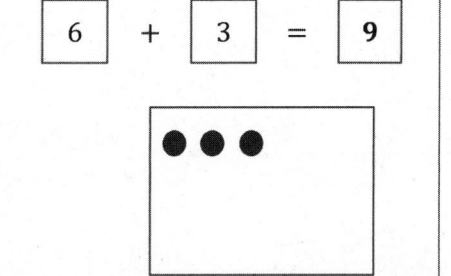

I used my 5-group cards as a short-cut. I can draw the card.

Lesson 15: Count on up to 3 more using numeral and 5-group cards and fingers to track the change.

A STORY OF UNITS – TEKS EDITION

Lesson 15 Homework 1•1

Name _____ Date _____

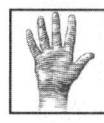

Use your 5-group cards or your fingers to count on to solve.

1. 5 + 3 = ☐

Show the shortcut you used to add.

6 + 2 = ☐

2. 6 + 2 = ☐

3. 7 + 3 = ☐

Show the strategy you used to add.

4. ☐ = 8 + 2

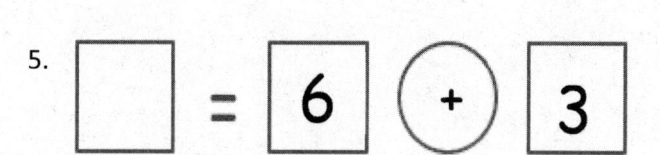

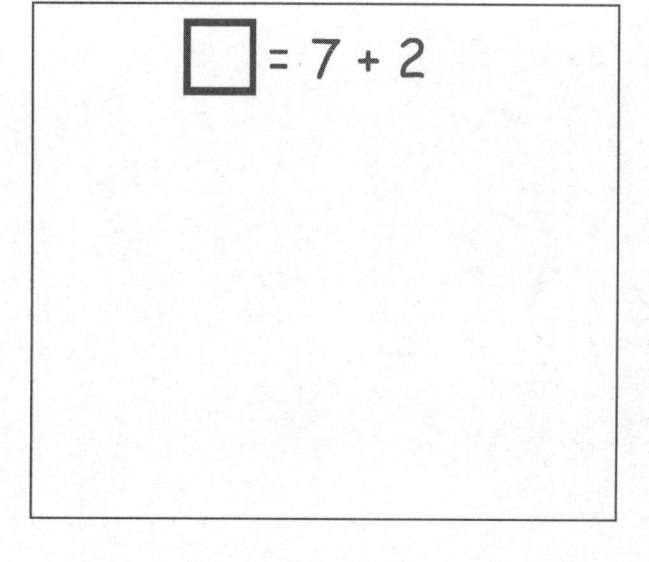

☐ = 7 + 2

5. ☐ = 6 + 3

6. ☐ = 7 + 2

Lesson 15: Count on up to 3 more using numeral and 5-group cards and fingers to track the change.

63

A STORY OF UNITS – TEKS EDITION

Lesson 16 Homework Helper 1•1

1. Use simple math drawings. Draw more to show 6 + ? = 9.

   > I can start at 6 and *count on* as I draw. I'll stop when I get to 9. Siiiiiiix...

   > ...7, 8, 9.

   $\boxed{6} + \boxed{3} = \boxed{9}$

   > I drew 3 more circles, so 6 + 3 = 9.

2. Use your 5-group cards to solve 4 + ? = 6.

   > I can start at 4 and draw the dots that are on the back of a 5-group card. Fooour...

   4 [□□] = 6

   > ...5, 6.

   $\boxed{4} + \boxed{2} = \boxed{6}$

   > I drew 2 dots, so 4 + 2 = 6.

Lesson 16: Count on to find the unknown part in missing addend equations such as 6 + ___ = 9. Answer, "How many more to make 6, 7, 8, 9, and 10?"

65

A STORY OF UNITS – TEKS EDITION

Lesson 16 Homework 1•1

Name _____   Date _____

1. Use simple math drawings. Draw more to solve 4 + ? = 6.

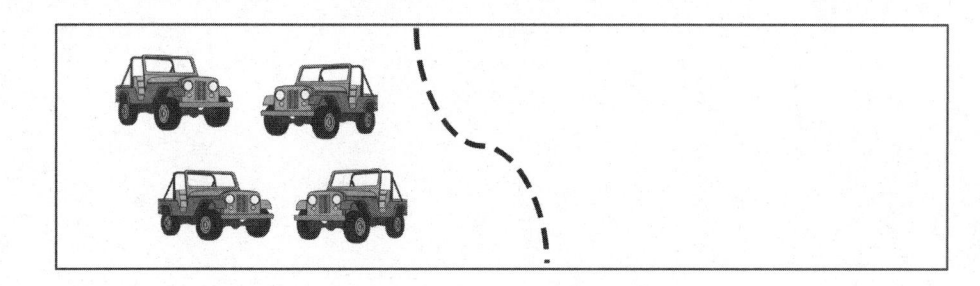

    = 6

    4 + ☐ = 6

2. Use your 5-group cards to solve 6 + ? = 8

    6   = 8

    6 + ☐ = 8

3. Use counting on to solve 7 + ? = 10

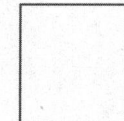

    7...

    7 + ☐ = 10

Lesson 16: Count on to find the unknown part in missing addend equations such as 6 + __ = 9. Answer, "How many more to make 6, 7, 8, 9, and 10?"

A STORY OF UNITS – TEKS EDITION

Lesson 17 Homework Helper 1•1

1. Match the equal dominoes. Then, write true number sentences.

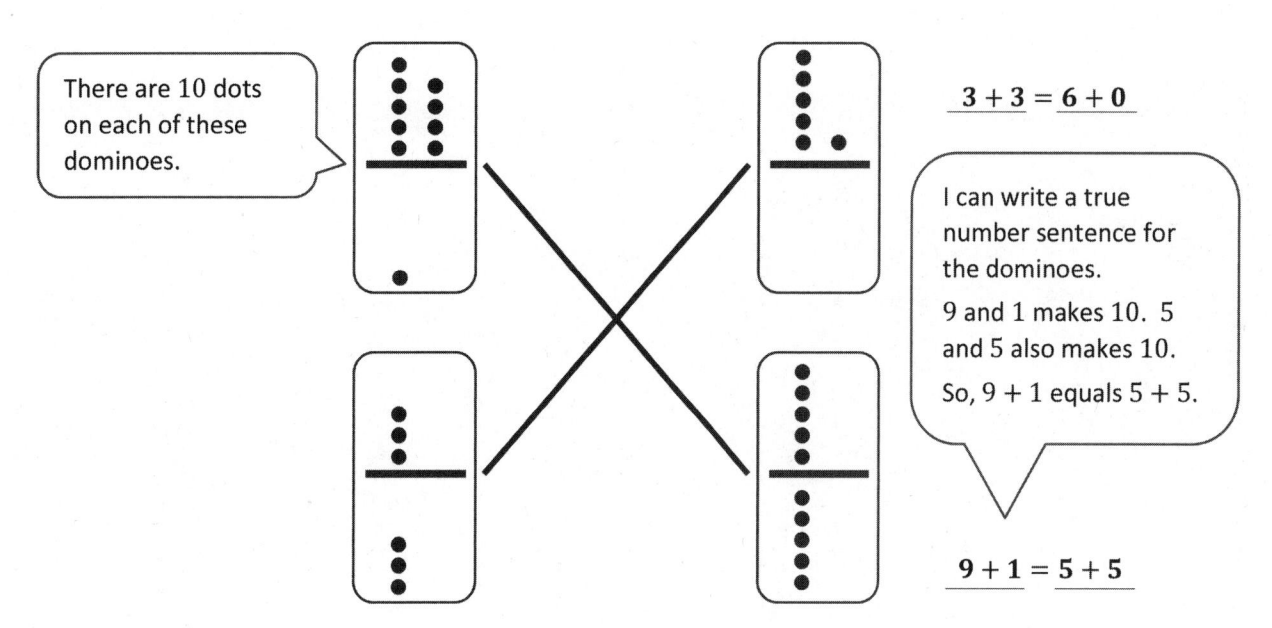

   > There are 10 dots on each of these dominoes.

   $3 + 3 = 6 + 0$

   > I can write a true number sentence for the dominoes.
   > 9 and 1 makes 10. 5 and 5 also makes 10. So, 9 + 1 equals 5 + 5.

   $9 + 1 = 5 + 5$

2. Find the expressions that are equal. Use the equal expressions to write true number sentences.

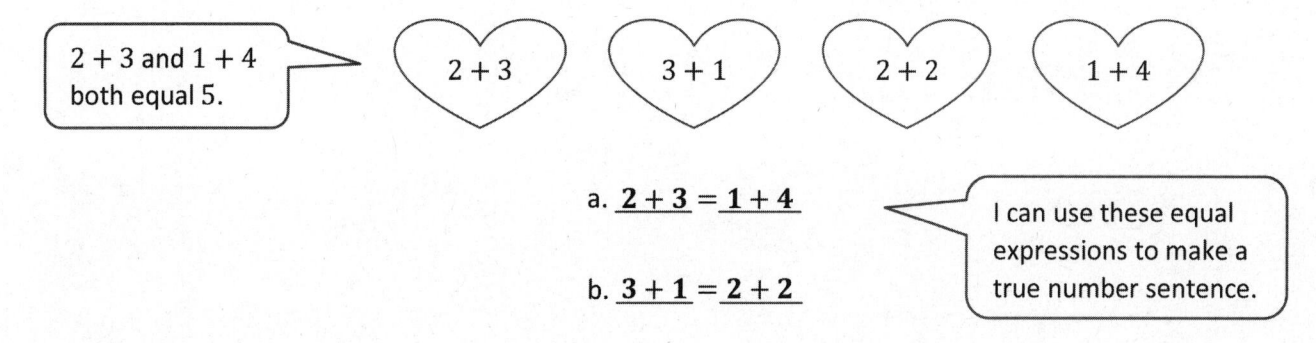

   > 2 + 3 and 1 + 4 both equal 5.

   $2 + 3$ $3 + 1$ $2 + 2$ $1 + 4$

   a. $2 + 3 = 1 + 4$

   b. $3 + 1 = 2 + 2$

   > I can use these equal expressions to make a true number sentence.

Lesson 17: Understand the meaning of the equal sign by pairing equivalent expressions and constructing true number sentences

69

A STORY OF UNITS – TEKS EDITION   Lesson 17 Homework   1•1

Name _____   Date _____

1. Match the equal dominoes. Then, write true number sentences.   4+4=5+3

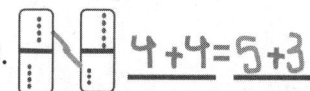

   a.

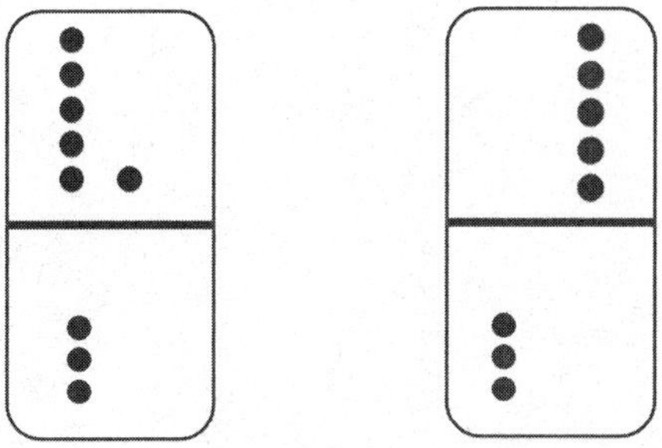

   b.

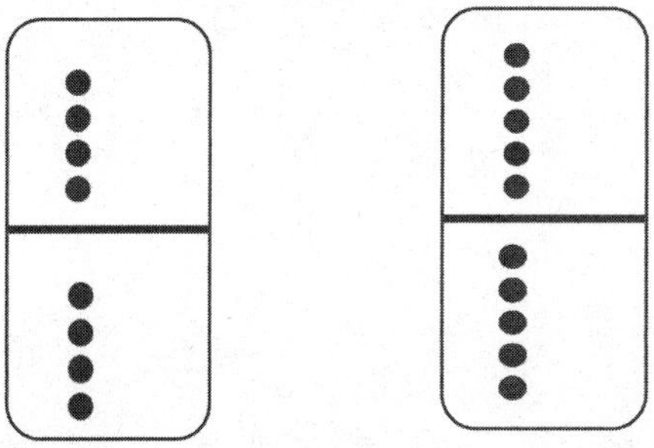

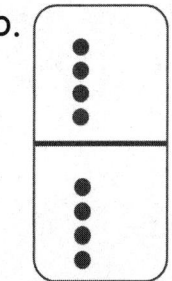

   c.

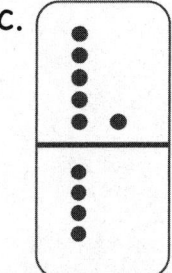

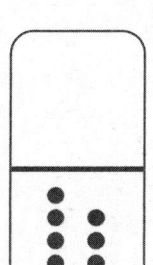

2. Find the expressions that are equal. Use the equal expressions to write true number sentences.

   5 + 2   8 + 2   4 + 3   7 + 3

   a. _____   _____

   b. _____   _____

Lesson 17: Understand the meaning of the equal sign by pairing equivalent expressions and constructing true number sentences

A STORY OF UNITS – TEKS EDITION   Lesson 18 Homework Helper   1•1

1. The pictures below are not equal. Make the pictures equal, and write a true number sentence.

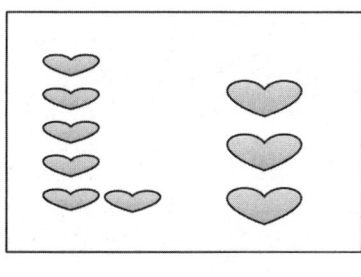

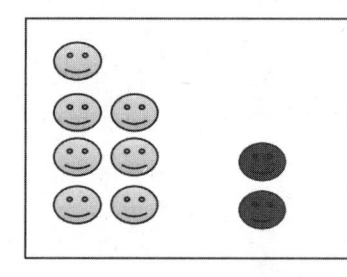

   __6 + 3__ = __7 + 2__

   > I know that 6 + 3 equals 9. I can count 7 smiley faces. If I draw 2 more smiley faces, I can make a true number sentence because 7 + 2 also equals 9.

2. Circle the true number sentence(s), and rewrite the false sentence(s) to make it true.

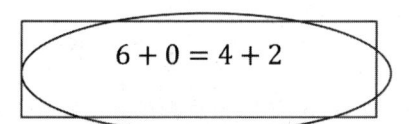

   (6 + 0 = 4 + 2)   5 + 1 = 6 + 1

   _____   5 + 2 = 6 + 1

   > I know that 5 + 1 is 6, and 6 + 1 is 7. 6 is not equal to 7. I can make this number sentence true by changing 5 + 1 to 5 + 2 so it equals 7.

3. Find the missing parts to make the number sentences true.

   7 + 1 = 4 + __4__   4 + 3 = __5__ + 2

   > I know that 7 + 1 equals 8. So, the other side must also equal 8 for this to be a true number sentence. I know my doubles: 4 + 4 = 8. The missing part is 4.

Lesson 18: Understand the meaning of the equal sign by pairing equivalent expressions and constructing true number sentences.

Name _____ Date _____

1. The pictures below are not equal. Make the pictures equal, and write a true number sentence.

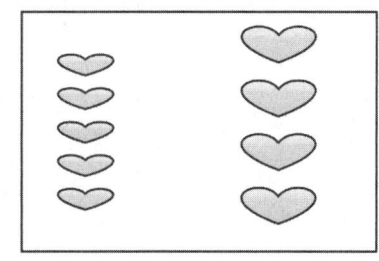

   _____ _____

2. Circle the true number sentences, and rewrite the false sentences to make them true.

   a. 4 = 4

   b. 5 + 1 = 6 + 1

   c. 3 + 2 = 5 + 0

   d. 6 + 2 = 4 + 4

   e. 3 + 3 = 6 + 2

   f. 9 + 0 = 7 + 2

   g. 4 + 3 = 2 + 4

   h. 8 = 8 + 0

   i. 6 + 3 = 5 + 4

3. Find the missing part to make the number sentences true.

a.

8 + 0 = ___ + 4

b.

7 + 2 = 9 + ___

c.

5 + 2 = 4 + ___

d.

5 + ___ = 6 + 0

e.

6 + ___ = 4 + 3

f.

5 + 4 = ___ + 3

A STORY OF UNITS – TEKS EDITION   Lesson 19 Homework Helper   1•1

1. Use the picture to write a number bond. Then, write the matching number sentences.

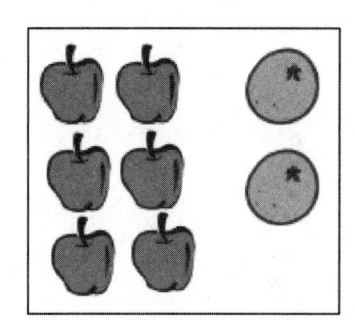

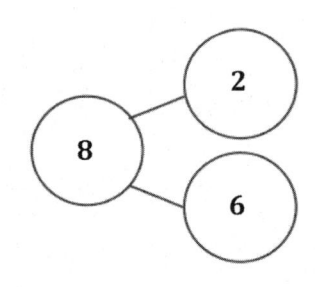

   $\underline{2} + \underline{6} = \underline{8}$

   $\underline{6} + \underline{2} = \underline{8}$

   > I can add in any order, but it is easier to start at 6 and count on 2. Siiiix, seven, eight! I love the counting on strategy!

2. Write the number sentences to match the number bonds.

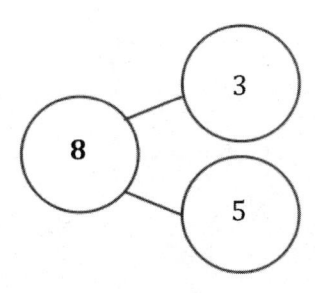

   $\underline{3} + \underline{5} = \underline{8}$

   $\underline{5} + \underline{3} = \underline{8}$

   > For both number sentences, the parts are 3 and 5, and the total is 8. The order of the addends doesn't matter when I solve.

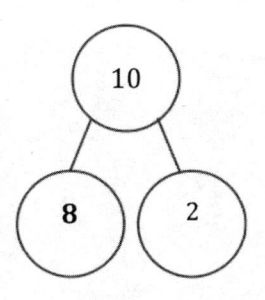

   $\underline{8} + \underline{2} = \underline{10}$

   $\underline{2} + \underline{8} = \underline{10}$

   > Since 10 is the total and one part is 2, I know the other part must be 8. I know my partners to 10, and I can add them in any order, 8 + 2 or 2 + 8.

Lesson 19: Represent the same story scenario with addends repositioned (the commutative property).

77

A STORY OF UNITS – TEKS EDITION   Lesson 19 Homework   1•1

Name _____   Date _____

1. Use the picture to write a number bond. Then, write the matching number sentences.

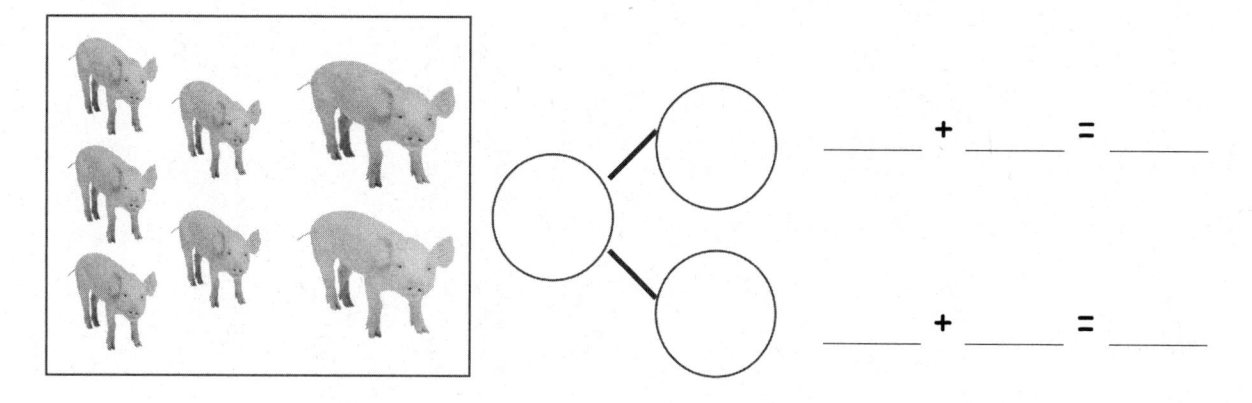

____ + ____ = ____

____ + ____ = ____

2. Write the number sentences to match the number bonds.

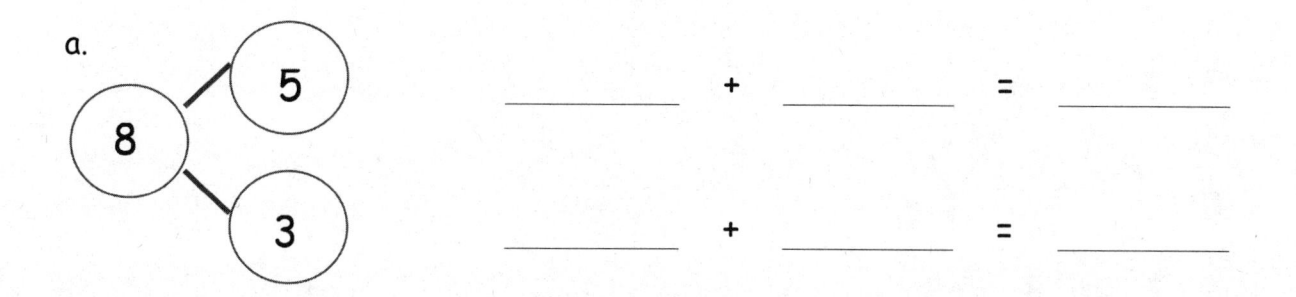

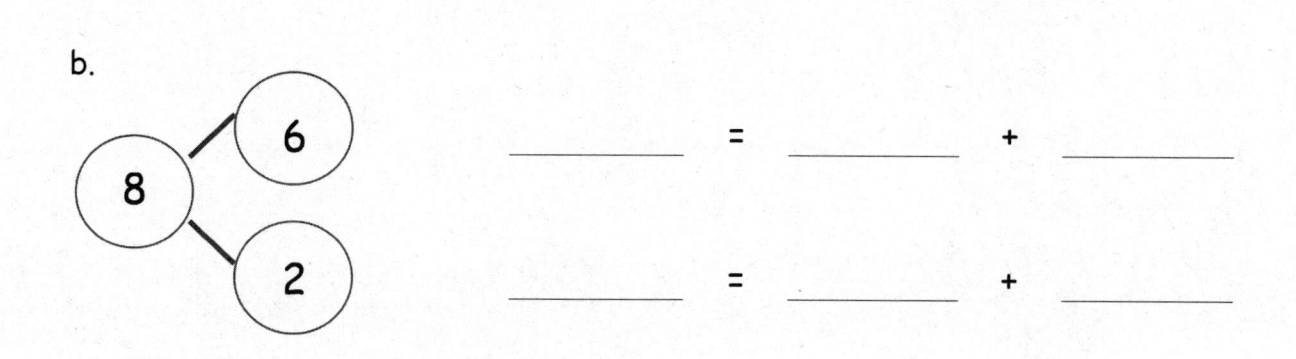

a. 8, 5, 3

____ + ____ = ____

____ + ____ = ____

b. 8, 6, 2

____ = ____ + ____

____ = ____ + ____

Lesson 19: Represent the same story scenario with addends repositioned (the commutative property).

79

A STORY OF UNITS – TEKS EDITION Lesson 19 Homework 1•1

c.

( ) — 8
     \
      2

___ + ___ = ___

___ + ___ = ___

d.

7
/ \
( ) 5

___ + ___ = ___

___ + ___ = ___

e.

10 — ( )
    \
     3

___ = ___ + ___

___ = ___ + ___

f.

9 — ( )
   \
    3

___ + ___ = ___

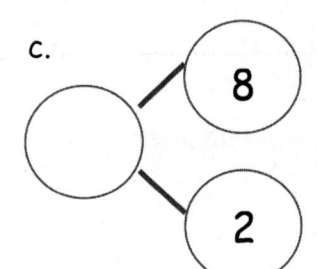

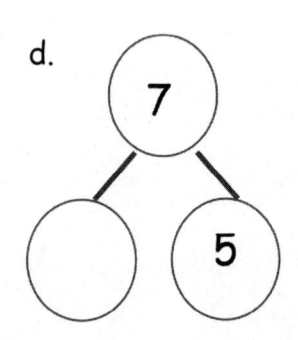

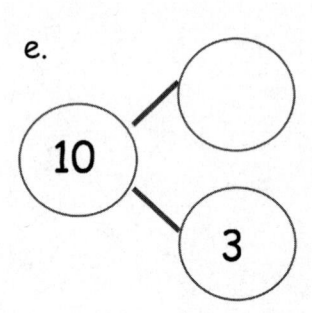

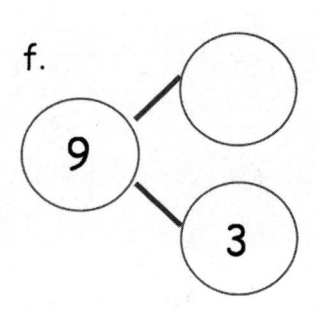

___ + ___ = ___

Lesson 19: Represent the same story scenario with addends repositioned (the commutative property).

A STORY OF UNITS – TEKS EDITION   Lesson 20 Homework Helper   1•1

1. Color the larger part, and complete the number bond. Write the number sentence, starting with the larger part.

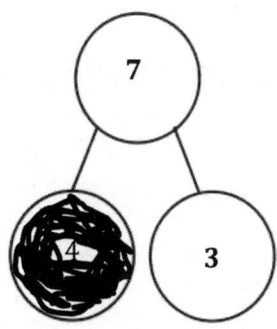

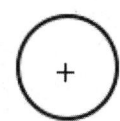

   [backpack with 4] [3 pencils]   Number bond: 7 → 4 (colored), 3

   $\boxed{4} \ (+) \ \boxed{3} \ = \ \boxed{7}$

   > 4 + 3 is the same amount as 3 + 4. It's a lot faster for me to count on from the larger addend: foooouur, five, six, seven.

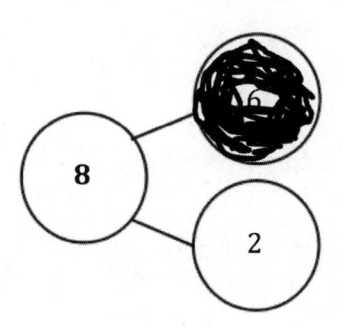

   Number bond: 8 → 6 (colored), 2

   $\underline{6} + \underline{2} = \underline{8}$

   > When I start with the larger addend, 6, I don't have to count on as much: Siiiix, seven, eight!

   Lesson 20: Apply the commutative property to count on from a larger addend.   81

A STORY OF UNITS – TEKS EDITION

Lesson 20 Homework 1•1

Name _____ Date _____

Color the larger part, and complete the number bond.
Write the number sentence, starting with the larger part.

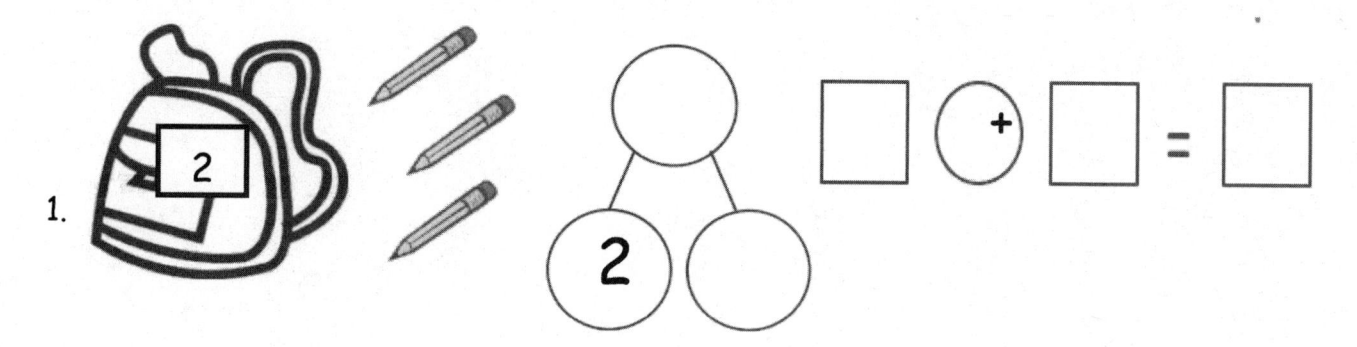

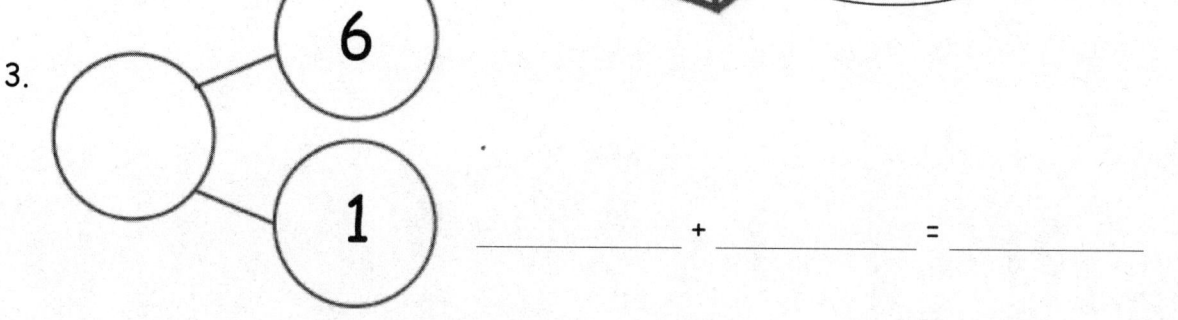

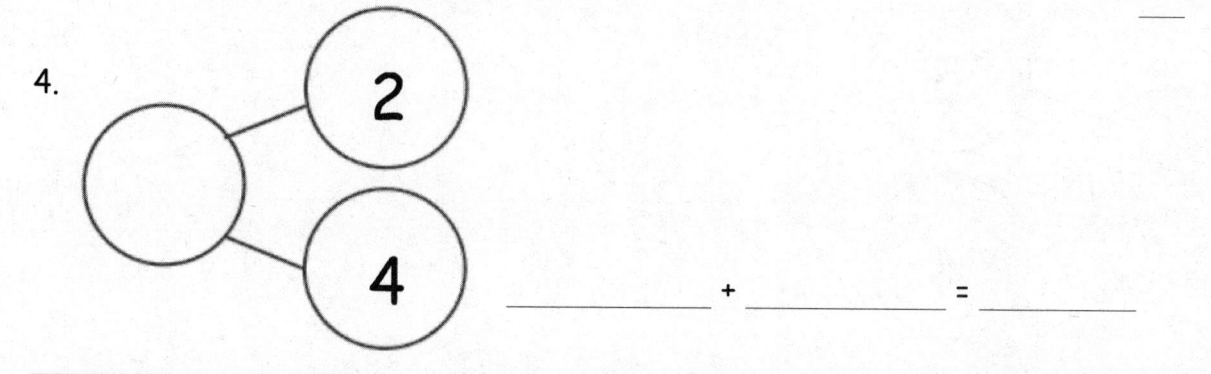

3 + 1 = 4

1. [backpack with 2, 3 pencils] [number bond: top empty, 2 and empty] ☐ + ☐ = ☐

2. ☐ + ☐ = ☐   [grocery bag 7, strawberry & lemon on plate] [number bond: 7, 7 and empty]

3. [number bond: empty, 6, 1]   _____ + _____ = _____

4. [number bond: empty, 2, 4]   _____ + _____ = _____

Lesson 20: Apply the commutative property to count on from a larger addend.

83

5.

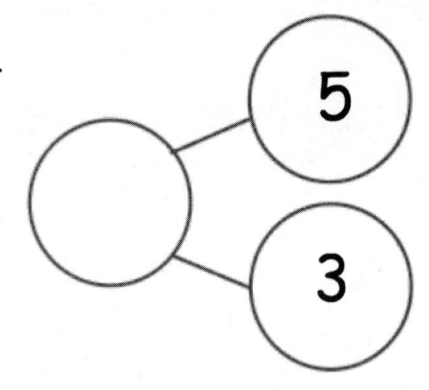

_____ + _____ = _____

6.

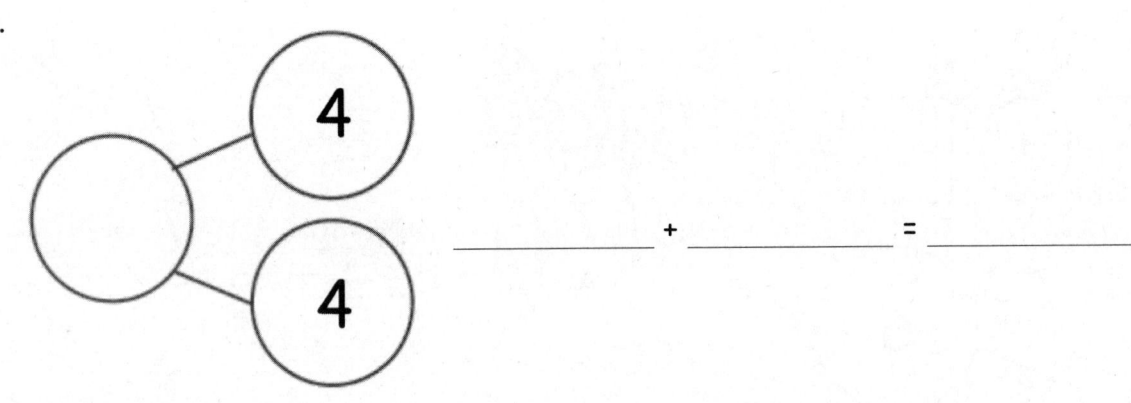

_____ + _____ = _____

7.

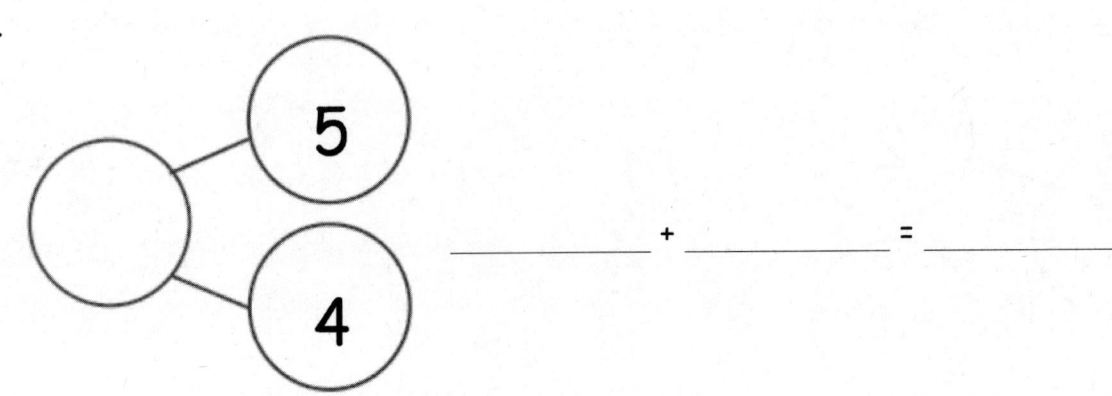

_____ + _____ = _____

Lesson 20: Apply the commutative property to count on from a larger addend.

A STORY OF UNITS – TEKS EDITION

Lesson 21 Homework Helper   1•1

1. Draw the 5-group card to show a double. Write the number sentence to match the card.

   [card: 4 / 4]

   > I can add the same number two times, like 4 + 4 = 8. This is called a doubles fact. I can picture flashing doubles fingers in my mind... 4 and 4 makes 8.

   4 + 4 = 8

2. Fill in the 5-group card in order from least to greatest, double the number, and write the number sentences.

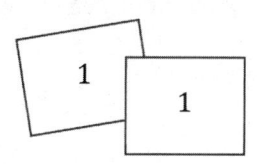

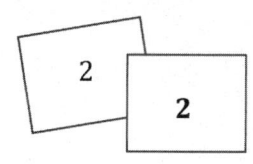

   [cards: 1, 1]   [cards: 2, 2]

   > I know my doubles facts: 1 + 1 = 2. 2 + 2 = 4. The next one would be 3 + 3 = 6. It's just like counting by 2s: 2, 4, 6.

   1 + 1 = 2   2 + 2 = 4

3. Match the top cards to the bottom cards to show doubles plus 1.

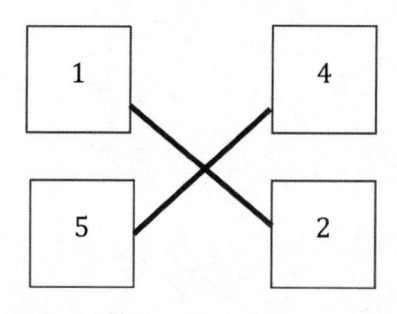

   [1]   [4]
     ╲ ╱
     ╱ ╲
   [5]   [2]

   > Since I know that 4 + 4 = 8, then I know my doubles plus 1, 4 + 5 = 9. I can picture the 5-group cards to help me solve. The doubles plus 1 fact has just 1 more dot!

4. Solve the number sentence. Write the doubles fact that helped you solve the double plus 1.

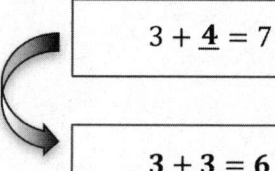

   3 + **4** = 7

   3 + 3 = 6

   > 3 + 4 is related to 3 + 3 because it's making doubles and adding 1 more. There is a doubles fact hiding inside 3 + 4.

Lesson 21: Visualize and solve doubles and doubles plus 1 with 5-group cards.

85

A STORY OF UNITS – TEKS EDITION

Lesson 21 Homework 1•1

Name _____ Date _____

1. Draw the 5-group card to show a double. Write the number sentence to match the cards.

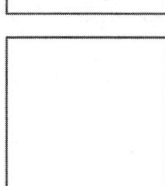

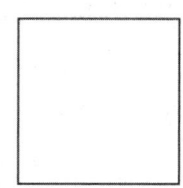

   a. 4

   b. 3

   c. 5

2. Fill in the 5-group cards in order from least to greatest, double the number, and write the number sentences.

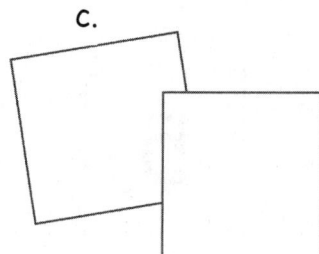

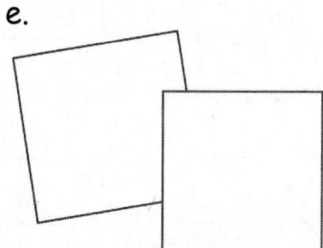

   a. 1, 1

   b. 2

   c.

   d. 4

   e.

Lesson 21: Visualize and solve doubles and doubles plus 1 with 5-group cards.

87

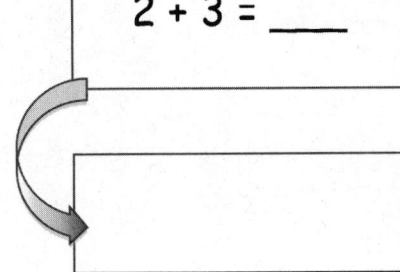

A STORY OF UNITS – TEKS EDITION   Lesson 21 Homework   1•1

3. Solve the number sentences.

a. 3 + 3 = ___

b. 5 + ___ = 10

c. 1 + ___ = 2

d. 4 = ___ + 2

e. 8 = 4 + ___

4. Match the top cards to the bottom cards to show doubles plus 1.

a. 1   b. 4   c. 3   d. 2

5   2   3   4

5. Solve the number sentences. Write the double fact that helped you solve the double plus 1.

a. 2 + 3 = ___

b. 3 + ___ = 7

c. 4 + ___ = 9

A STORY OF UNITS – TEKS EDITION

Lesson 22 Homework Helper 1•1

Solve the problems without counting all. Color the boxes using the key.

Step 1: Color the problems with " + 1" or " 1 +" blue (B).
Step 2: Color the remaining problems with " + 2" or " 2 +" green (G).
Step 3: Color the remaining problems with " + 3" or " 3 +" yellow (Y).

a. **B** 8 + 1 = __9__	b. **B** 9 + __1__ = 10	c. **Y** 3 + 5 = __8__	d. **Y** 5 + 3 = __8__
e. **G** 6 + __2__ = 8	f. **Y** 4 + __3__ = 7	g. **B** 6 + 1 = __7__	h. **G** __2__ + 8 = 10

In parts c and d, it's like when we added in a different order. The total is the same!

In parts a and b, I can add 1 each time, and the total goes up by 1. It's just the next counting number!

In parts e and h, I can think of counting on by 2 each time.

Lesson 22: Look for and make use of repeated reasoning on the addition chart by solving and analyzing problems with common addends.

89

A STORY OF UNITS – TEKS EDITION   Lesson 22 Homework   1•1

Name _____   Date _____

Solve the problems without counting all. Color the boxes using the key.

Step 1: Color the problems with "+ 1" or "1 +" blue.
Step 2: Color the remaining problems with "+ 2" or "2 +" green.
Step 3: Color the remaining problems with "+ 3" or "3 +" yellow.

a. 7 + 1 = ___	b. 8 + ___ = 9	c. 3 + 1 = ___	d. 5 + 3 = ___
e. 5 + ___ = 7	f. 4 + ___ = 7	g. 6 + 3 = ___	h. 8 + ___ = 10
i. 2 + 1 = ___	j. 1 + ___ = 2	k. 1 + ___ = 4	l. 6 + 2 = ___
m. 3 + ___ = 6	n. 6 + ___ = 7	o. 3 + 2 = ___	p. 5 + 1 = ___
q. 2 + 2 = ___	r. 4 + ___ = 6	s. 4 + 1 = ___	t. 7 + 2 = ___
u. 2 + ___ = 3	v. 9 + 1 = ___	w. 7 + 3 = ___	x. 1 + ___ = 3

Lesson 22: Look for and make use of repeated reasoning on the addition chart by solving and analyzing problems with common addends.

| A STORY OF UNITS – TEKS EDITION | | Lesson 23 Homework Helper | 1•1 |

Fill in the missing box, and find the totals for all of the expressions. Use your completed addition chart to help you.

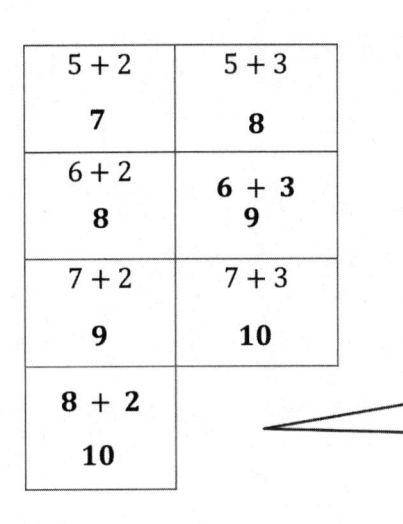

5 + 2 7	5 + 3 8
6 + 2 8	6 + 3 9
7 + 2 9	7 + 3 10
8 + 2 10	

> I can see which expressions equal 8. They make a diagonal line. Look, totals for 9 and 10 do the same thing!

> I know that 8 + 2 is the missing expression in this column because these are +2 facts. When I look at the first addend, I see it increases by 1 each time: 5, 6, 7, ... so 8 comes next!

3 + 4 7	3 + 5 8	3 + 6 9
4 + 4 8	4 + 5 9	4 + 6 10
5 + 4 9	5 + 5 10	
6 + 4 10		

> The totals at the bottom of each column are 10. They look like a staircase!

> I know to write 4 + 6 in this box. In each row, the first addend stays the same, but the second addend increases by 1, so 4 + 4, 4 + 5, 4 + 6. The totals increase by 1, too: 8, 9, 10.

Lesson 23: Look for and make use of structure on the addition chart by looking for and coloring problems with the same total.

Name _____   Date _____

Fill in the missing box, and find the totals for all of the expressions. Use your completed addition chart to help you.

1.

1 + 2	1 + 3
2 + 2	
3 + 2	3 + 3

2.

6 + 1	6 + 2
7 + 1	
	8 + 2
9 + 1	

3.

4 + 4	4 + 5	
5 + 4		
6 + 4		

4.

2 + 4		2 + 6
	3 + 5	

A STORY OF UNITS – TEKS EDITION   Lesson 24 Homework Helper   1•1

1. Solve and sort the number sentences. One number sentence can go in more than one place when you sort.

   | 5 + 1 = __6__ | 5 + 2 = __7__ | 2 + 3 = __5__ |

   | 3 + 3 = __6__ | 10 = 1 + __9__ | __9__ = 5 + 4 |

Doubles	Doubles +1	+1	+2	Mentally visualized 5-groups
3 + 3 = 6	2 + 3 = 5	5 + 1 = 6	5 + 2 = 7	5 + 1 = 6
4 + 4 = 8	9 = 5 + 4	10 = 1 + 9	8 + 2 = 10	5 + 2 = 7
	3 + 4 = 7			9 = 5 + 4

   Look at the Doubles +1 facts! I can put them in order, and they build: 2 + 3, 3 + 4, 4 + 5. The totals increase by 2 each time: 5, 7, 9.

   I can see the 5-group card. I see a row of 5 dots on the top and 4 dots on the bottom.

2. Write your own number sentences, and add them to the chart.

   | 4 + 4 = 8 | | 8 + 2 = 10 | | 3 + 4 = 7 |

   3 + 3 and 4 + 4 are related facts. 4 + 4 is the next doubles fact.

   3 + 4 is a double +1 fact. The doubles fact is 3 + 3 = 6. 4 is 1 more than 3, so I know 3 + 4 = 7.

   Lesson 24:   Practice to build fluency with facts to 10.

A STORY OF UNITS – TEKS EDITION   Lesson 24 Homework   1•1

Name _____   Date _____

Solve and sort the number sentences. One number sentence can go in more than one place when you sort.

5 + 1 = _____	6 + 2 = _____	2 + 3 = _____
3 + 3 = _____	7 + 1 = _____	2 + 2 = _____
_____ = 4 + 4	8 + 2 = _____	3 + 4 = _____
_____ = 5 + 4	10 = 1 + _____	_____ = 5 + 2

Doubles	Doubles +1	+1	+2	Mentally visualized 5-groups

Write your own number sentences, and add them to the chart.

Lesson 24: Practice to build fluency with facts to 10.

Solve and practice math facts.

1 + 0	1 + 1	1 + 2	1 + 3	1 + 4	1 + 5	1 + 6	1 + 7	1 + 8	1 + 9
2 + 0	2 + 1	2 + 2	2 + 3	2 + 4	2 + 5	2 + 6	2 + 7	2 + 8	
3 + 0	3 + 1	3 + 2	3 + 3	3 + 4	3 + 5	3 + 6	3 + 7		
4 + 0	4 + 1	4 + 2	4 + 3	4 + 4	4 + 5	4 + 6			
5 + 0	5 + 1	5 + 2	5 + 3	5 + 4	5 + 5				
6 + 0	6 + 1	6 + 2	6 + 3	6 + 4					
7 + 0	7 + 1	7 + 2	7 + 3						
8 + 0	8 + 1	8 + 2							
9 + 0	9 + 1								
10 + 0									

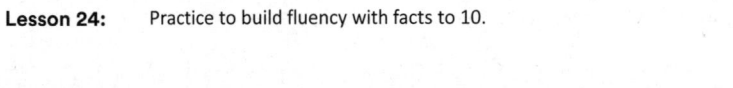

A STORY OF UNITS – TEKS EDITION

Lesson 25 Homework Helper 1•1

1. Break the total into parts. Write a number bond and addition and subtraction number sentences to match the story.

   Jane caught 9 fish. She caught 7 fish before she ate lunch. How many fish did she catch after lunch?

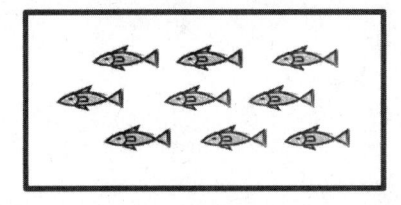

   $7 + 2 = 9$

   $9 - 7 = 2$

   Jane caught __2__ fish after lunch.

   > I can use counting on and an addition sentence to solve. Seeeven, eight, nine!

   > Since I know the whole and one part, I can also use subtraction to find the other part.

   Number bond: 9 → 7, 2

2. Draw a picture to solve the math story.

   Jenna had 3 strawberries. Sanjay gave her more strawberries. Now, Jenna has 8 strawberries. How many strawberries did Sanjay give her?

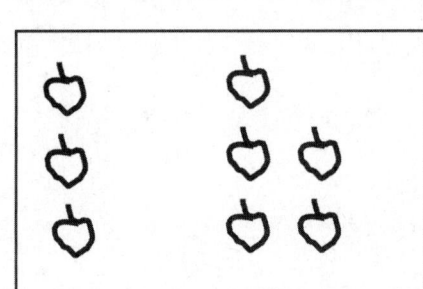

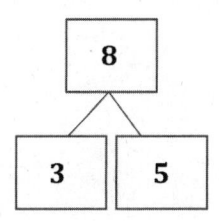

   Number bond: 8 → 3, 5

   $3 + 5 = 8$

   $8 - 3 = 5$

   Sanjay gave her __5__ strawberries.

   > 8 stands for the total number of strawberries Jenna has. 3 stands for the strawberries Jenna had at first. I know the total and one part. I need to find the other part.

   > Both of my number sentences match my number bond! Addition and subtraction both have parts and a whole.

Lesson 25: Solve *add to with change unknown* math stories with addition, and relate to subtraction. Model with materials, and write corresponding number sentences.

A STORY OF UNITS – TEKS EDITION Lesson 25 Homework 1•1

Name _____ Date _____

Break the total into parts. Write a number bond and addition and subtraction number sentences to match the story.

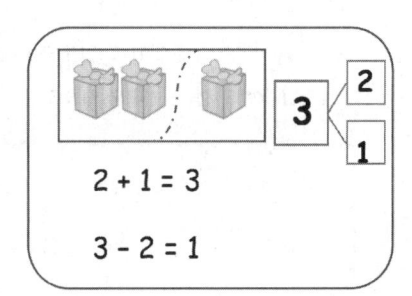

2 + 1 = 3

3 - 2 = 1

1. Six flowers bloomed on Monday. Some more bloomed on Tuesday. Now, there are 8 flowers. How many flowers bloomed on Tuesday?

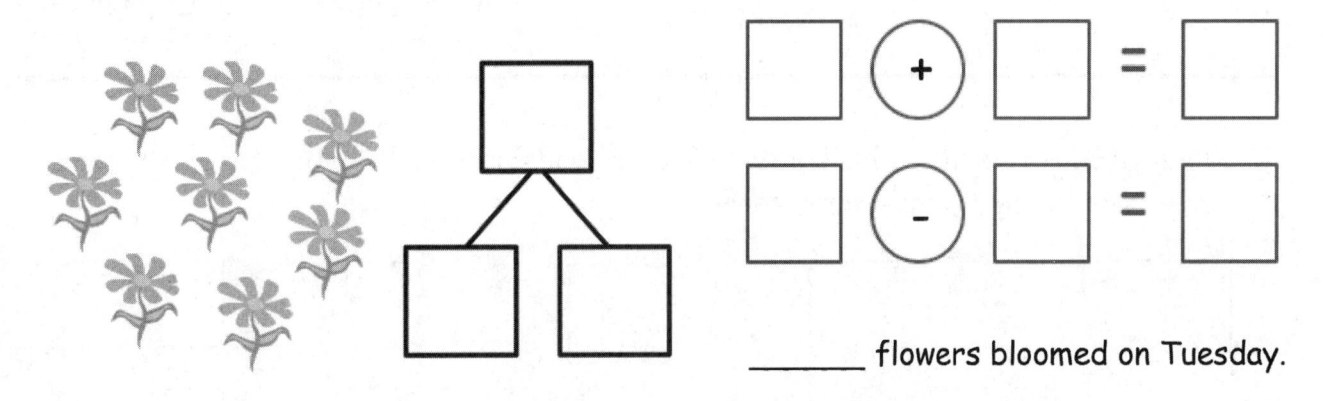

   ☐ + ☐ = ☐

   ☐ - ☐ = ☐

   _____ flowers bloomed on Tuesday.

2. Below are the balloons that Mom bought. She bought 4 balloons for Bella, and the rest of the balloons were for Jim. How many balloons did she buy for Jim?

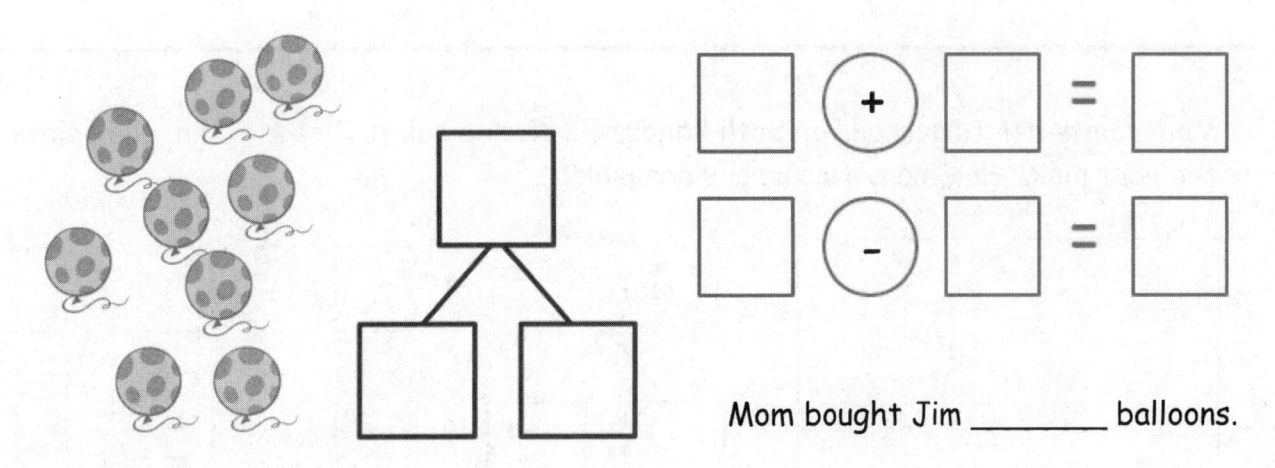

   ☐ + ☐ = ☐

   ☐ - ☐ = ☐

   Mom bought Jim _____ balloons.

Lesson 25: Solve *add to with change unknown* math stories with addition, and relate to subtraction. Model with materials, and write corresponding number sentences.

Draw a picture to solve the math story.

3. Missy buys some cupcakes and 2 cookies. Now, she has 6 desserts. How many cupcakes did she buy?

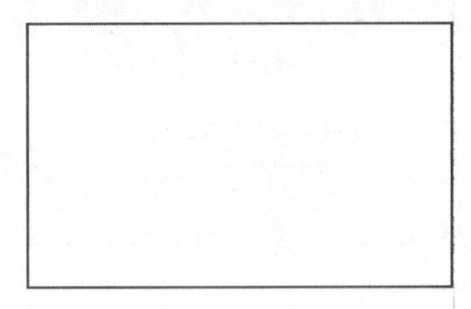

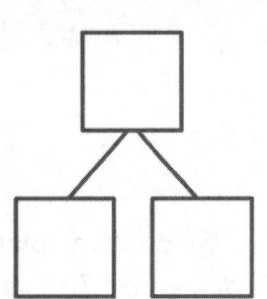

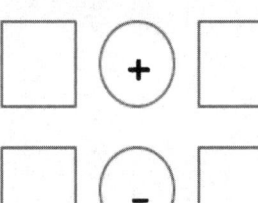

☐ + ☐ = ☐

☐ − ☐ = ☐

Missy bought _____ cupcakes.

4. Jim invited 9 friends to his party. Three friends arrived late, but the rest came early. How many friends came early?

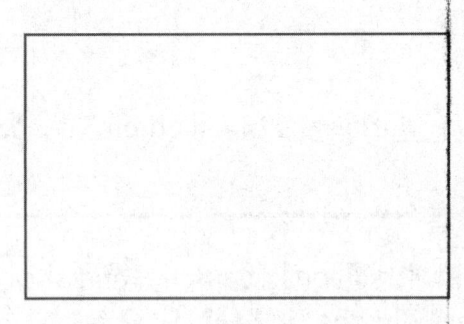

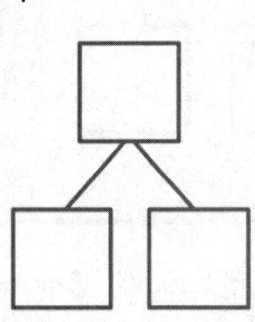

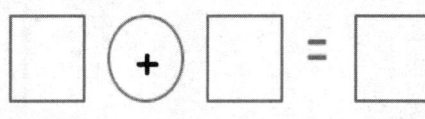

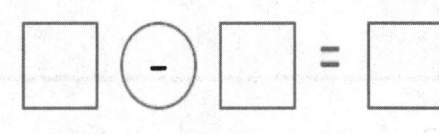

☐ + ☐ = ☐

☐ − ☐ = ☐

_____ friends came early.

5. Mom paints her fingernails on both hands. First, she paints 2 red. Then, she paints the rest pink. How many fingernails are pink?

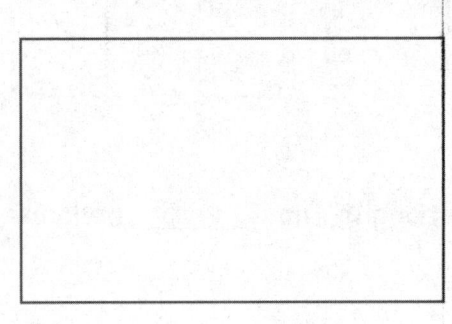

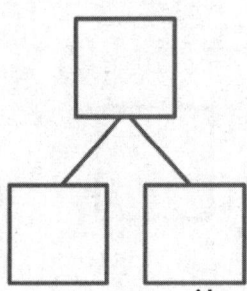

☐ + ☐ = ☐

☐ − ☐ = ☐

Mom paints _____ fingernails pink.

A STORY OF UNITS – TEKS EDITION　　　　Lesson 26 Homework Helper　1•1

1. Use the number path to solve.

> To solve 7 – 5, I can think "5 plus something equals 7." I can start at 5 and count up until I get to 7. It takes 2 hops to get to 7, so 7 – 5 = 2. That's the same as thinking 5 + 2 = 7.

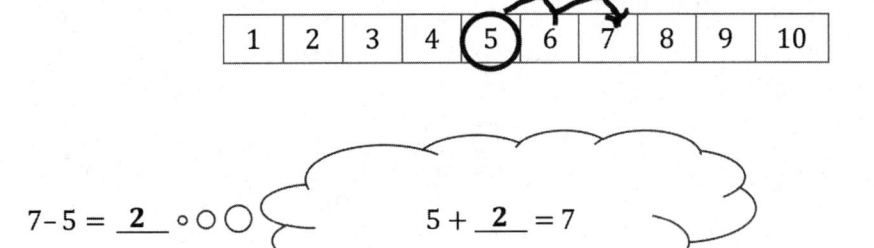

| 1 | 2 | 3 | 4 | ⑤ | 6 | 7 | 8 | 9 | 10 |

7 – 5 = __2__　　　　5 + __2__ = 7

2. Use the number path to help you solve.

| 1 | 2 | 3 | 4 | 5 | 6 | 7 | 8 | 9 | 10 |

9 – 6 = __3__　　　　6 + __3__ = 9

> Now that I have practiced, I don't actually have to circle the number on the number path and draw the arrows. I can just use my pencil point to imagine the hops. To solve 9 – 6, I'm going to start at 6 and count up until I get to 9. That's like solving my missing addend problems. 6 + 3 = 9, so 9 – 6 = 3.

Lesson 26: Count on using the number path to find an unknown part.

105

A STORY OF UNITS – TEKS EDITION   Lesson 26 Homework   1•1

Name _____   Date _____

Use the number path to solve.

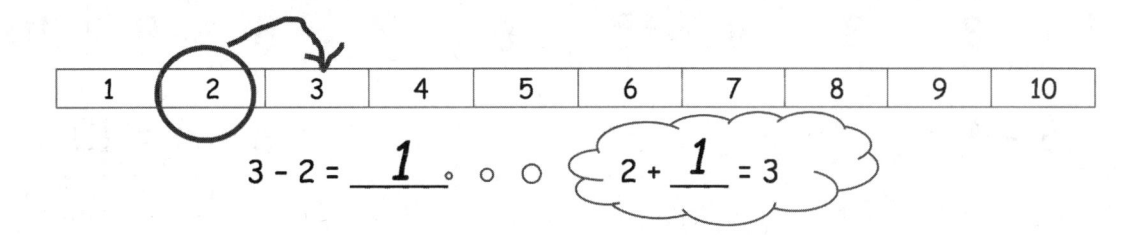

| 1 | 2 | 3 | 4 | 5 | 6 | 7 | 8 | 9 | 10 |

3 - 2 = __1__   2 + __1__ = 3

1.
| 1 | 2 | 3 | 4 | 5 | 6 | 7 | 8 | 9 | 10 |

5 - 3 = _____   3 + ___ = 5

2.
| 1 | 2 | 3 | 4 | 5 | 6 | 7 | 8 | 9 | 10 |

a. 8 - 6 = _____   6 + _____ = 8

b. 7 - 4 = _____   4 + _____ = 7

c. 8 - 2 = _____

d. 9 - 6 = _____

Lesson 26:   Count on using the number path to find an unknown part.

A STORY OF UNITS – TEKS EDITION | Lesson 26 Homework | 1•1

Use the number path to solve. Match the addition sentence that can help you.

| 1 | 2 | 3 | 4 | 5 | 6 | 7 | 8 | 9 | 10 |

3. a. 6 - 4 = ____

    6 + 4 = 10

    b. 9 - 5 = ____

    10 = 7 + 3

    c. 10 - 6 = ____

    4 + 5 = 9

    d. 10 - 7 = ____

    6 = 4 + 2

4. Write an addition and subtraction number sentence for the number bond. You may use the number path to solve.

| 1 | 2 | 3 | 4 | 5 | 6 | 7 | 8 | 9 | 10 |

a. 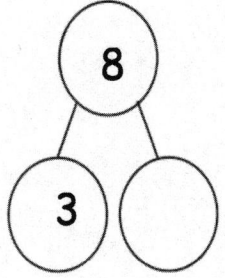 8 / 3, ___

b. 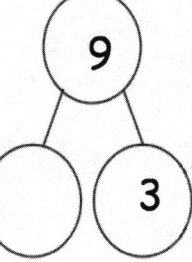 9 / 3, ___

Lesson 26: Count on using the number path to find an unknown part.

A STORY OF UNITS – TEKS EDITION

Lesson 27 Homework Helper 1•1

1. Use the number path to complete the number bond, and then write an addition and a subtraction sentence to match.

| 1 | 2 | 3 | 4 | 5 | 6 | 7 | 8 | 9 | 10 |

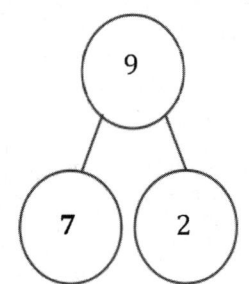

Number bond: 9 at top, 7 and 2 at bottom.

$9 - 2 = 7$

$2 + 7 = 9$

> I can count back from 9 using 2 hops. I get to 7. That means 7 is the missing part of the number bond. $9 - 2 = 7$ and $2 + 7 = 9$.

2. Solve the number sentences. Pick the best way to solve. Check the box.

Count on → Count back ←

a. $9 - 1 = \underline{\ 8\ }$ — Count back: **X**

b. $8 - 7 = \underline{\ 1\ }$ — Count on: **X**

> For $9 - 1$, it's faster to count back, since that would just be 1 hop back. $9 - 1 = 8$.
>
> 8 and 7 are close together though, so it's faster to count on from 7. $7 + 1 = 8$, so that's just 1 hop forward.

Lesson 27: Count on using the number path to find an unknown part.

109

A STORY OF UNITS – TEKS EDITION　　　　Lesson 27 Homework Helper　　1•1

3. Solve the number sentence. Pick the best way to solve. Use the number path to show why.

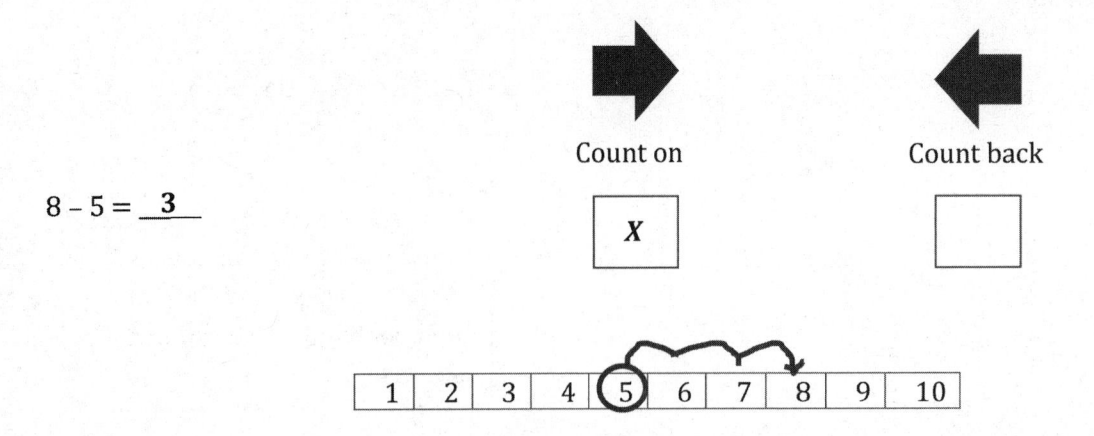

➡ Count on　　　⬅ Count back

8 − 5 = __3__

[X]　　[ ]

| 1 | 2 | 3 | 4 | ⑤ | 6 | 7 | 8 | 9 | 10 |

I counted __on__ because it needed fewer hops.

> 8 and 5 are numbers that are close together. It's faster to count on when the numbers are close together. I'll start at 5 and count 3 hops to get to 8.

4. Make a math drawing or write a number sentence to show why this is best.

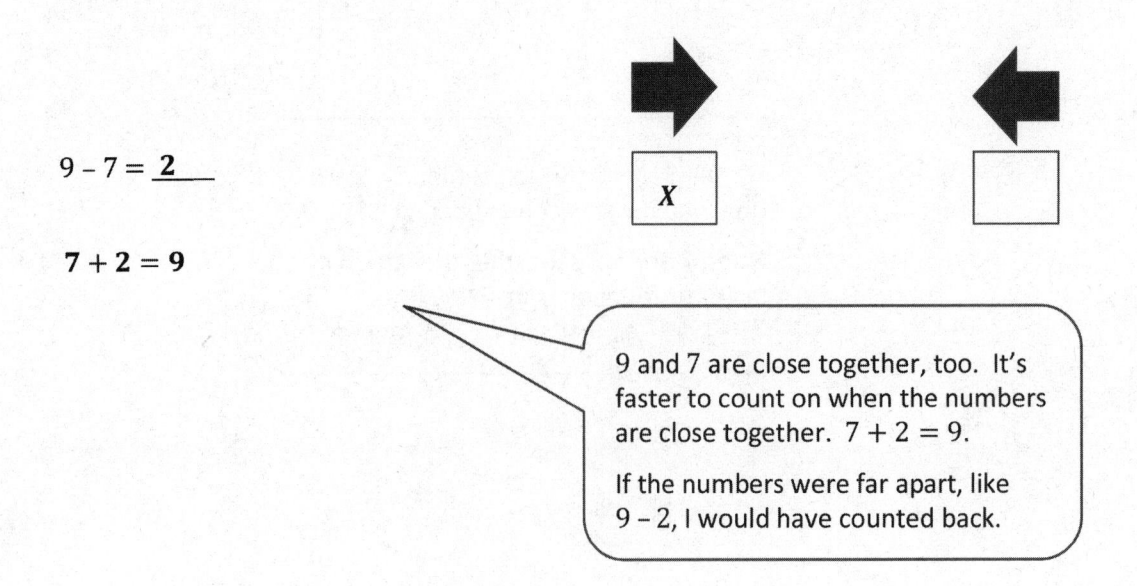

➡　　　⬅

9 − 7 = __2__

[X]　　[ ]

7 + 2 = 9

> 9 and 7 are close together, too. It's faster to count on when the numbers are close together. 7 + 2 = 9.
>
> If the numbers were far apart, like 9 − 2, I would have counted back.

Lesson 27: Count on using the number path to find an unknown part.

A STORY OF UNITS – TEKS EDITION   Lesson 27 Homework   1•1

Name _____   Date _____

Use the number path to complete the number bond, and write an addition and a subtraction sentence to match.

1.
Number Path

| 1 | 2 | 3 | 4 | 5 | 6 | 7 | 8 | 9 | 10 |

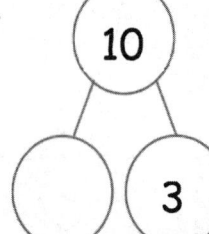

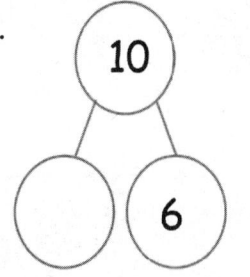

a. 10 / ○ \ 3   _____
                  _____

b. 10 / ○ \ 6   _____
                  _____

2. Solve the number sentences. Pick the best way to solve. Check the box.

➡ Count on   ⬅ Count back

a. 9 - 7 = _____   ☐   ☐

b. 8 - 2 = _____   ☐   ☐

c. 7 - 5 = _____   ☐   ☐

Lesson 27: Count on using the number path to find an unknown part.

A STORY OF UNITS – TEKS EDITION

Lesson 27 Homework 1•1

3. Solve the number sentence. Pick the best way to solve. Use the number path to show why.

Count on   **Count back**

a. 7 – 5 = _____   ☐   ☐

| 1 | 2 | 3 | 4 | 5 | 6 | 7 | 8 | 9 | 10 |

I counted _____ because it needed fewer hops.

b. 9 – 1 = _____   ☐   ☐

| 1 | 2 | 3 | 4 | 5 | 6 | 7 | 8 | 9 | 10 |

I counted _____ because it needed fewer hops.

c. 10 – 8 = ___   ☐   ☐

Make a math drawing or write a number sentence to show why this is best.

Lesson 27: Count on using the number path to find an unknown part.

A STORY OF UNITS – TEKS EDITION   Lesson 28 Homework Helper   1•1

Read the story. Make a math drawing to solve.

Bob buys 9 new toy cars. He takes 2 out of the bag. How many cars are still in the bag?

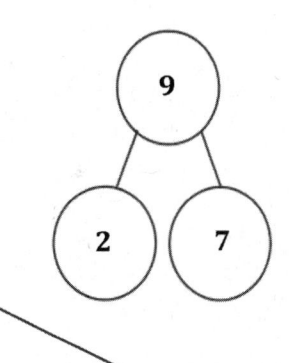

OOOOOOO⊖⊖

Number bond: 9 → 2 and 7

$\underline{9} - \underline{2} = \underline{7}$

<u>7</u> cars are still in the bag.

> I can draw 9 circles for the 9 toy cars. Then I can cross off 2 because Bob took 2 out of his bag. There are 7 circles left. Those are the 7 cars that are still in the bag.
>
> In the number bond, I can show 9 is the total number of cars. The part that was taken out is 2. The part that is still left is 7.
> $9 - 2 = 7$.

Lesson 28: Solve *take from with result unknown* math stories with math drawings, true number sentences, and statements, using horizontal marks to cross off what is taken away.

Name _____   Date _____

Read the story. Make a math drawing to solve.

Sample: 3-2=1

1. There were 6 hot dogs on the grill. Two finish cooking and are removed. How many hot dogs remain on the grill?

   (6)

   6 - ___ = ___

   There are ___ hot dogs remaining on the grill.

2. Bob buys 8 new toy cars. He takes 3 out of the bag. How many cars are still in the bag?

   ___ - ___ = ___

   ___ cars are still in the bag.

3. Kira sees 7 birds in the tree. Three birds fly away. How many birds are still in the tree?

   ___ - ___ = ___

   ___ birds are still in the tree.

Lesson 28: Solve *take from with result unknown* math stories with math drawings, true number sentences, and statements, using horizontal marks to cross off what is taken away.

A STORY OF UNITS – TEKS EDITION   Lesson 28 Homework   1•1

4. Brad has 9 friends over for a party. Six friends get picked up. How many friends are still at the party?

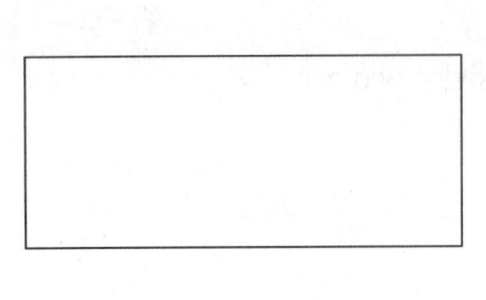

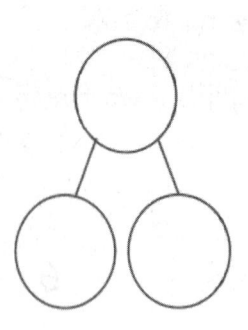

____ - ____ = ____

____ friends are still at the party.

5. Jordan was playing with 10 cars. He gave 7 to Kate. How many cars is Jordan playing with now?

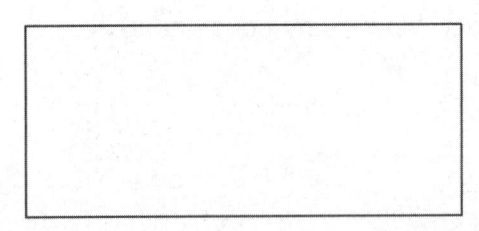

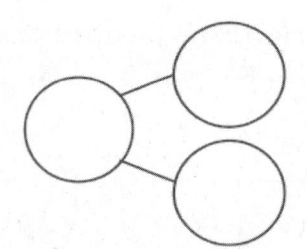

____ - ____ = ____

Jordan is playing with ____ cars now.

6. Tony takes 4 books from the bookshelf. There were 10 books on the shelf to start. How many books are on the shelf now?

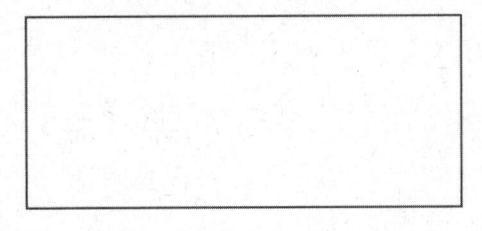

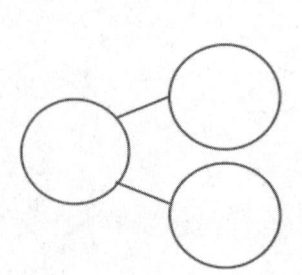

____ - ____ = ____

____ books are on the shelf now.

116   Lesson 28:   Solve *take from with result unknown* math stories with math drawings, true number sentences, and statements, using horizontal marks to cross off what is taken away.

A STORY OF UNITS – TEKS EDITION

Lesson 29 Homework Helper

1•1

Read the math stories. Make math drawings to solve.

Tom has a box of 8 crayons. 3 crayons are red. How many crayons are not red?

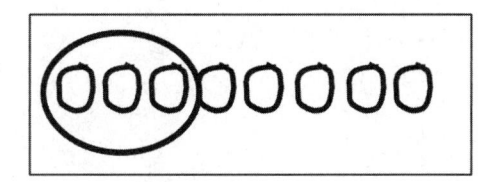

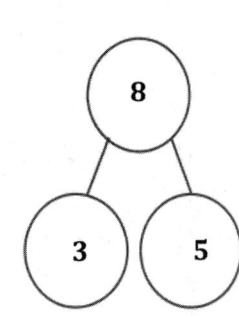

$\underline{8} - \underline{3} = \underline{5}$

$\underline{5}$ crayons are not red.

> I can draw 8 circles for the 8 crayons. I can circle the 3 crayons that are red. That leaves 5 crayons that are not red.
>
> In the number bond, I can show 8 is the total number of crayons. The part that is red is 3. The part that is not red is 5.
>
> $8 - 3 = 5.$
>
> The statement for my answer is <u>5 *crayons are not red*</u>.

Lesson 29: Solve *take apart with addend unknown* math stories with math drawings, equations, and statements, circling the known part to find the unknown.

A STORY OF UNITS — TEKS EDITION

Lesson 29 Homework 1•1

Name _____ Date _____

Read the math stories. Make math drawings to solve. ⬚⬚⬚⬚⬚ 5 - 4 = 1

1. Tom has a box of 7 crayons. Five crayons are red. How many crayons are not red?

   ___ - ___ = ___

   ____ crayons are not red.

2. Mary picks 8 flowers. Two are daisies. The rest are tulips. How many tulips does she pick?

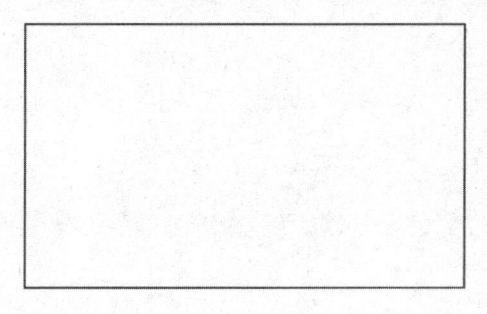

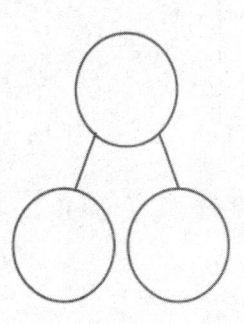

   ___ - ___ = ___

   Mary picks ____ tulips.

3. There are 9 pieces of fruit in the bowl. Four are apples. The rest are oranges. How many pieces of fruit are oranges?

   ___ - ___ = ___

   The bowl has ___ oranges.

Lesson 29: Solve *take apart with addend unknown* math stories with math drawings, equations, and statements, circling the known part to find the unknown.

4. Mom and Ben make 10 cookies. Six are stars. The rest are round. How many cookies are round?

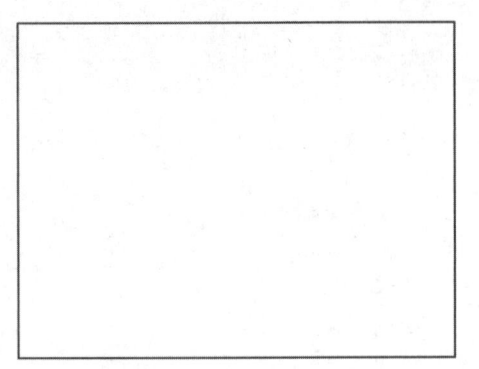

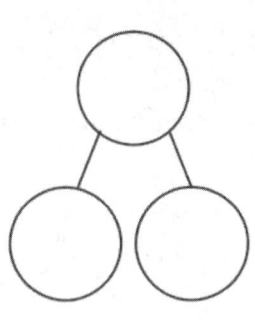

___ - ___ = ___

There are __ round cookies.

5. The parking lot has 7 spaces. Two cars are parked in the lot. How many more cars can park in the lot?

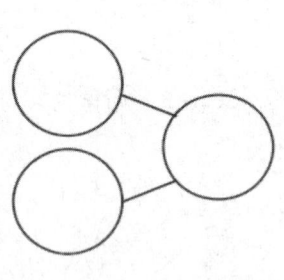

___ - ___ = ___

__ more cars can park in the lot.

6. Liz has 2 fingers with bandages. How many fingers are not hurt?

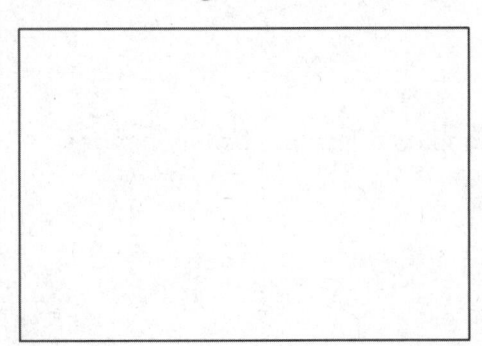

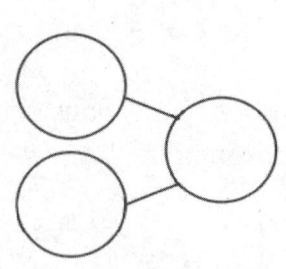

___ - ___ = ___

Write a statement for your answer:
_____

A STORY OF UNITS – TEKS EDITION

Lesson 30 Homework Helper 1•1

Solve the math story. Draw and label a picture number bond to solve. Circle the unknown number.

Lee has a total of 9 cars. He puts 6 in the toy box and takes the rest to his friend's house. How many cars does Lee take to his friend's house?

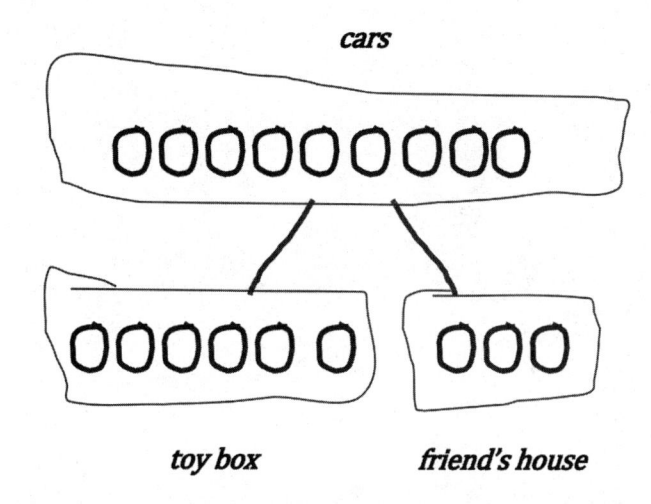

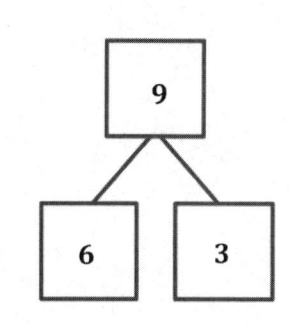

cars

OOOOOO OOO

OOOOO O   OOO

toy box   *friend's house*

```
      9
     / \
    6   3
```

6 + 3 = 9

9 - 6 = 3

Lee takes __3__ cars to his friend's house.

> I can draw 9 circles for the 9 cars. I put 6 circles in the toy box, and then I count on as I draw more cars in the box that says "friend's house." That's 3 more cars. Lee takes 3 cars to his friend's house.
>
> In the number bond, I can show 9 is the total number of cars. The part that he puts in the toy box is 6, and the part that he takes with him is 3.
>
> 6 + 3 = 9.
>
> 9 − 6 = 3.

Lesson 30: Solve *add to with change unknown* math stories with drawings, relating addition and subtraction.

Name _____ Date _____

Solve the math stories. Draw and label a picture number bond to solve. Circle the unknown number.

1. Grace has a total of 7 dolls. She puts 2 in the toy box and takes the rest to her friend's house. How many dolls does she take to her friend's house?

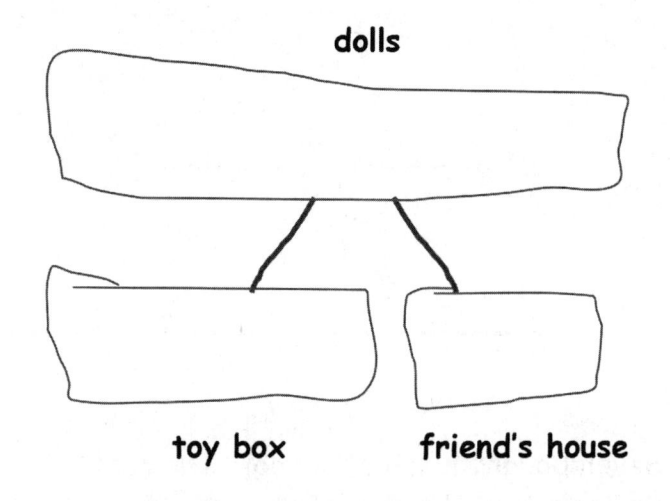

dolls

toy box   friend's house

Grace takes _____ dolls to her friend's house.

_____ + _____ = 7

7 − _____ = _____

2. Jack can invite 8 friends to his birthday party. He makes 3 invitations. How many invitations does he still need to make?

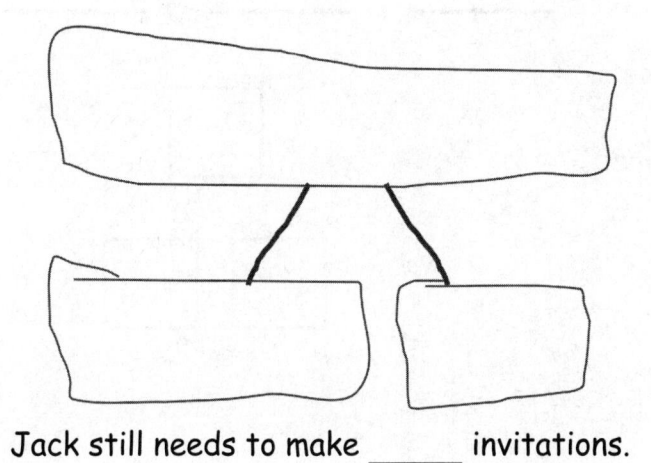

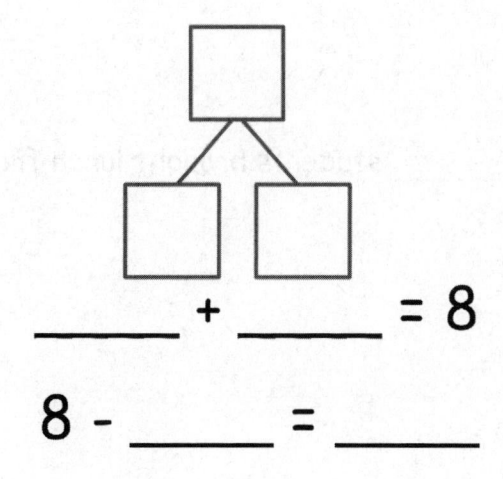

Jack still needs to make _____ invitations.

_____ + _____ = 8

8 − _____ = _____

Lesson 30: Solve *add to with change unknown* math stories with drawings, relating addition and subtraction.

3. There are 9 dogs at the park. Five dogs play with balls. The rest are eating bones. How many dogs are eating bones?

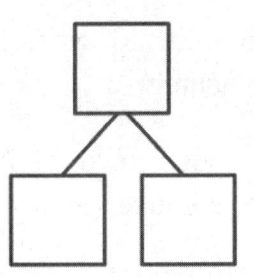

____ + ____ = 9

____ - ____ = ____

_____ dogs are eating bones.

4. There are 10 students in Jim's class. Seven bought lunch at school. The rest brought lunch from home. How many students brought lunch from home?

____ + ____ = ____

____ - ____ = ____

_____ students brought lunch from home.

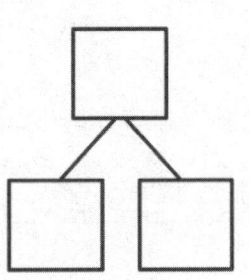

A STORY OF UNITS – TEKS EDITION

Lesson 31 Homework Helper 1•1

The sample problem below shows two possible number sentences. Both are considered reasonable and correct. If your child chooses to write the first number sentence, suggest that he/she draw a box around the solution.

Make a math drawing, and circle the part you know. Cross out the unknown part. Complete the number sentence and number bond.

A store had 6 shirts on the rack. Now, there are 2 shirts on the rack. How many shirts were sold?

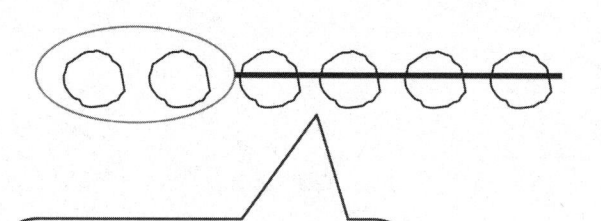

> I know how to make a quick math drawing! I can circle 2 dots since there are 2 shirts left. I can draw a line through 4 shirts. My line looks like one big subtraction sign!

> When I solve with subtraction, I can still use a number bond to think of addition. If 6 is the total and 2 is one part, the other part must be 4.

$6 - \boxed{4} = 2$

$6 - 2 = \boxed{4}$

> I can write 6 minus the mystery box because I don't know how many shirts were sold. But I know that 2 shirts ended up on the rack. 6 minus something is 2.

___4___ shirts were sold.

> Both of my number sentences match my number bond! Addition and subtraction both have parts and a whole.

Lesson 31: Solve *take from with change unknown* math stories with drawings.

A STORY OF UNITS – TEKS EDITION   Lesson 31 Homework 1•1

Name _____   Date _____

Make a math drawing, and circle the part you know.
Cross out the unknown part.
Complete the number sentence and number bond.

Sample 3 - 1 = 2

1. Missy gets 6 presents for her birthday. She unwraps some. Four are still wrapped. How many presents did she unwrap?

    Missy unwrapped _____ presents.

    6 - ☐ = ☐

2. Ann has a box of 8 markers. Some fall on the floor. Six are still in the box. How many markers fell on the floor?

    _____ markers fell on the floor.

    ☐ - ☐ = ☐

3. Nick makes 7 cupcakes for his friends. Some cupcakes were eaten. Now, there are 5 left. How many cupcakes were eaten?

    _____ cupcakes were eaten.

    ☐ - ☐ = ☐

Lesson 31:   Solve *take from with change unknown* math stories with drawings.

4. A dog has 8 bones. He hides some. He still has 5 bones. How many bones are hidden?

_____ bones are hidden.

☐ (-) ☐ = ☐

5. The cafeteria table can seat 10 students. Some of the seats are taken. Seven seats are empty. How many seats are taken?

_____ seats are taken.

☐ (-) ☐ = ☐

6. Ron has 10 sticks of gum. He gives one stick to each of his friends. Now, he has 3 sticks of gum left. How many friends did Ron share with?

Ron shared with _____ friends.

☐ (-) ☐ = ☐

| A STORY OF UNITS – TEKS EDITION | Lesson 32 Homework Helper 1•1 |

1. Match the math stories to the number sentences that tell the story. Make a math drawing to solve.

   a.

   There are 9 flowers in a vase.
   5 are red.
   The rest are yellow.
   How many flowers are yellow?

   OOOOO OOOO

   [3] (+) [7] = [10]

   [10] (−) [3] = [7]

   b.

   There are 10 apples in a basket.
   3 are red.
   The rest are green.
   How many apples are green?

   ⊙⊙⊙OOOOOOO

   [5] (+) [4] = [9]

   [9] (−) [5] = [4]

   > For the first math story, I can draw 5 circles for the red flowers, and then I can count on and draw until I have 9 circles. I see that there are 4 yellow flowers. This story goes with the second box of number sentences. I can tell because the total number of flowers is 9 flowers. 5 plus 4 equals 9, and 9 take away 5 equals 4.
   >
   > For the second math story, I can draw 10 circles for the 10 apples. Then I can circle the 3 that are red. That leaves 7 green apples. This goes with the first box of number sentences. 3 plus 7 equals 10. 10 minus 3 equals 7.

Lesson 32: Solve *put together/take apart with addend unknown* math stories.

A STORY OF UNITS – TEKS EDITION

Lesson 32 Homework Helper 1•1

2. Use the number bond to tell an addition and subtraction math story with pictures. Write an addition and subtraction number sentence.

> For my addition math story, I can draw 2 big pears and 4 little pears. There are 2 big pears and 4 little pears. How many pears do I have in all? That goes with the number sentence 2 plus 4 equals 6.

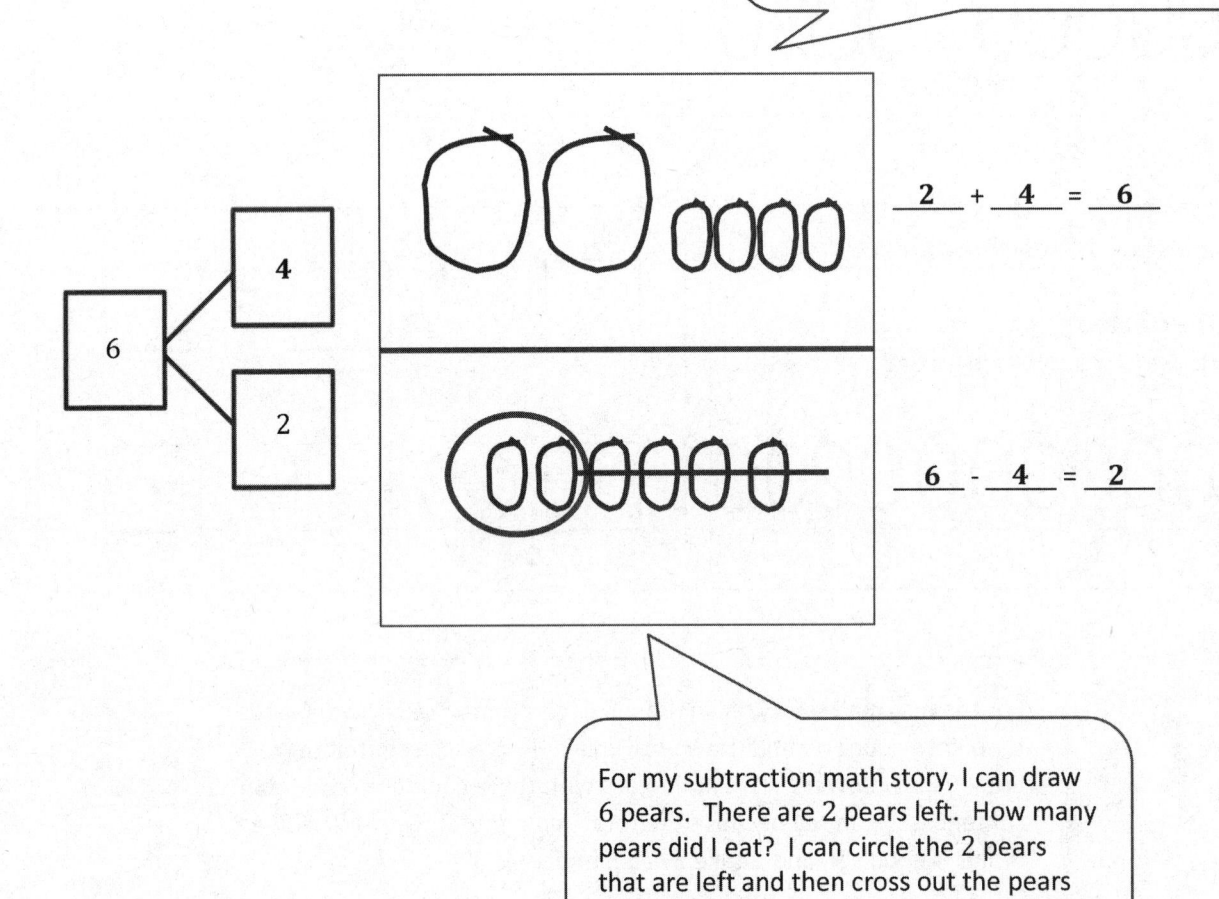

Number bond: 6 → 4, 2

_2_ + _4_ = _6_

_6_ - _4_ = _2_

> For my subtraction math story, I can draw 6 pears. There are 2 pears left. How many pears did I eat? I can circle the 2 pears that are left and then cross out the pears that I ate. That shows that I ate 4 pears. 6 minus 4 equals 2.

130 Lesson 32: Solve *put together/take apart with addend unknown* math stories.

© Great Minds PBC
TEKS Edition | greatminds.org/texas

EUREKA MATH
TEKS EDITION

A STORY OF UNITS – TEKS EDITION

Lesson 32 Homework 1•1

Name _____ Date _____

Match the math stories to the number sentences that tell the story. Make a math drawing to solve.

1. a.

There are 10 flowers in a vase.
6 are red.
The rest are yellow.
How many flowers are yellow?

☐ + ☐ = 9

9 − ☐ = ☐

b.

There are 9 apples in a basket.
6 are red.
The rest are green.
How many apples are green?

3 + ☐ = 10

10 − ☐ = ☐

c.

Kate has her fingernails painted.
3 have designs.
The rest are plain.
How many fingernails are plain?

6 + ☐ = 10

10 − 6 = ☐

Lesson 32: Solve *put together/take apart with addend unknown* math stories.

A STORY OF UNITS – TEKS EDITION

Lesson 32 Homework 1•1

Use the number bond to tell an addition and subtraction math story with pictures. Write an addition and subtraction number sentence.

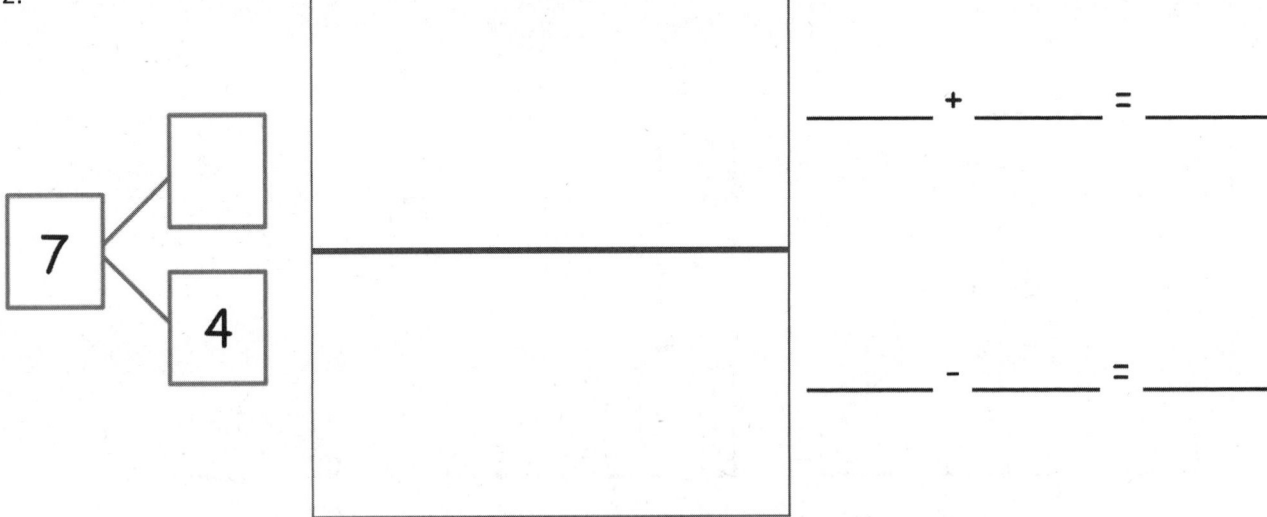

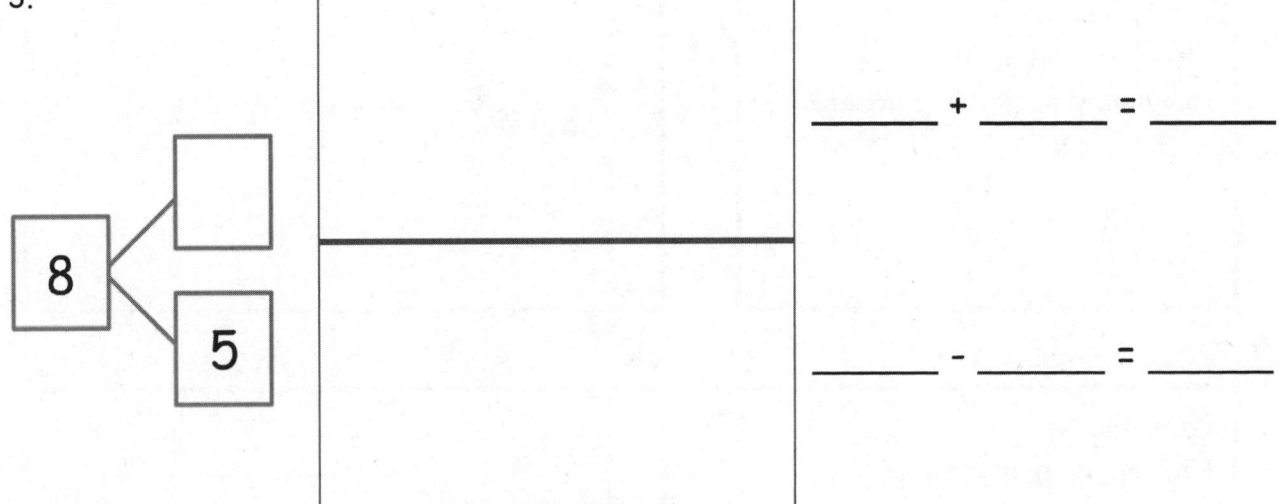

2.

7
□
4

_____ + _____ = _____

_____ − _____ = _____

3.

8
□
5

_____ + _____ = _____

_____ − _____ = _____

132 Lesson 32: Solve *put together/take apart with addend unknown* math stories.

A STORY OF UNITS – TEKS EDITION　　　Lesson 33 Homework Helper　　1•1

1. Show the subtraction. If you want, make a 5-group drawing for each problem.

   ●●●●●—

   5 – 1 = __4__　　　　5 – 0 = __5__

   > I wasn't sure about 5 – 1, so I drew it out, but I know 5 – 0 is 5, so I don't need to draw.

2. Show the subtraction. If you want, make a 5-group drawing like the model for each problem.

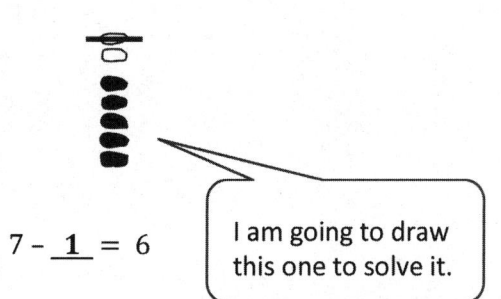

   7 – __1__ = 6　　　　10 – __0__ = 10

   > I am going to draw this one to solve it.

   > I know 10 – 0 = 10, so I am not going to draw this one.

3. Write the subtraction number sentence to match the 5-group drawing.

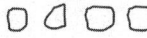

   ●●●●● ○○○○

   __9__ – __0__ = __9__

4. Fill in the missing number. Visualize your 5-groups to help you.

   9 – __1__ = 8　　　0 = 8 – __8__

   > I can imagine 9 circles in my mind. How much do I take away to have 8 left? Just 1. I can erase 1 of my 9 in my mind, and I would have 8 left.

   > This one is tricky, but I can solve it. 8 minus something has to equal 0. Both sides of the equal sign have to be the same amount. 8 – 8 is the same amount as 0.

Lesson 33: Model 0 less and 1 less pictorially and as subtraction number sentences.

Name _____ Date _____

Show the subtraction. If you want, use a 5-group drawing for each problem.

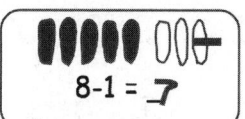

1.

9 − 1 = ____

2. ●●●●● ○○∅
    8 − 1 = 7

9 − 0 = ____

3.

6 − ____ = 6

4.

6 = 7 − ____

Show the subtraction. If you want, use a 5-group drawing like the model for each problem.

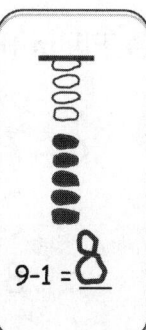

5.

9 − ____ = 9

6.

8 = 8 − ____

9 − 1 = 8

7.

10 − ____ = 9

8.

7 − ____ = 7

Write the subtraction number sentence to match the 5-group drawing.

9. ●●●●●̶○̶   10. ●●●●● ○ ○   11. ●●●●● ○ ○ ○̶

____ - ____ = ____   ____ - ____ = ____   ____ - ____ = ____

12.   13.

____ - ____ = ____   ____ - ____ = ____

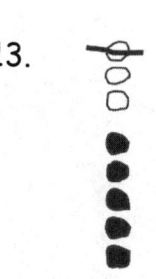

14. Fill in the missing number. Visualize your 5-groups to help you.

a. 7 - ____ = 6

b. 0 = 7 - ____

c. 8 - ____ = 7

d. 6 - ____ = 5

e. 8 = 9 - ____

f. 9 = 10 - ____

g. 10 - ____ = 10

h. 9 - ____ = 8

Lesson 33: Model 0 less and 1 less pictorially and as subtraction number sentences.

A STORY OF UNITS – TEKS EDITION

Lesson 34 Homework Helper 1•1

1. cross off to subtract.

    6 – 5 = __1__

2. Make a 5-group drawing like those above. Show the subtraction.

    1 = 5 – __4__   5 – __5__ = 0

3. Make a 5-group drawing like the model for each problem. Show the subtraction.

    9 – 9 = ◯

    7 – __6__ = 1

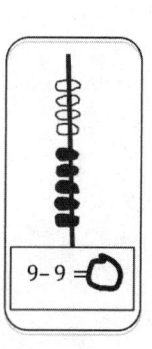

4. Write the subtraction number sentence to match the 5-group drawing.

    __8__ – __7__ = __1__

5. Fill in the missing numbers. Visualize your 5-groups to help you.

    7 – __6__ = 1   1 = 8 – __7__

Lesson 34: Model $n - n$ and $n - (n - 1)$ pictorially and as subtraction sentences.

Name _____   Date _____

Cross off to subtract.

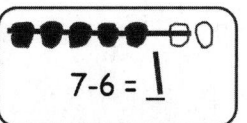

1. ●●●●● ○○○○○   2. ●●●●● ○○○○   7-6 = 1

   10 - 10 = ____   9 - 8 = ____

Make a 5-group drawing like those above. Show the subtraction.

3.   4.

   1 = ____ - 7   8 - ____ = 0

5.   6.

   0 = ____ - 7   6 - ____ = 1

Make a 5-group drawing like the model for each problem. Show the subtraction.

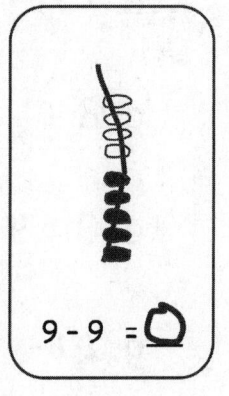

7.   8.

   9 - ___ = 1   0 = 8 - ___

                          9 - 9 = 0

Lesson 34: Model $n - n$ and $n - (n - 1)$ pictorially and as subtraction sentences.

Write the subtraction number sentence to match the 5-group drawing.

9.   10.   11.

___ - ___ = ___   ___ - ___ = ___   ___ - ___ = ___

12.

13.

___ - ___ = ___   ___ - ___ = ___

14. Fill in the missing number. Visualize your 5-groups to help you.

a. 7 - ____ = 0   b. 1 = 7 - ____

c. 8 - ____ = 1   d. 6 - ____ = 0

e. 0 = 9 - ____   f. 1 = 10 - ____

g. 10 - ____ = 0   h. 9 - ____ = 1

A STORY OF UNITS – TEKS EDITION

Lesson 35 Homework Helper 1•1

1. Solve the sets of number sentences. Look for easy groups to cross off.

> To take away 5, it's easiest to cross off the whole group of 5 black dots. I don't have to count them. Then I have 3 white dots left.

> To subtract 3, I can just cross off the three white dots. They are an easy group to see, and then I will be left with a group of 5. I don't have to count those dots because I know there are 5 black dots in my 5-group drawing.

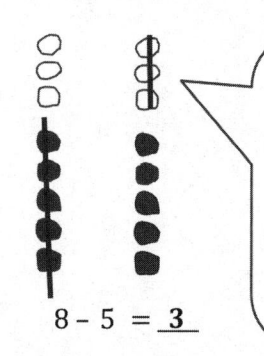

8 − 5 = __3__

8 − 3 = __5__

2. Subtract. Make a math drawing for each problem like the ones above. Write a number bond.

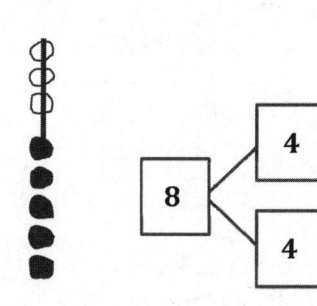

8 − 4 = __4__

> I can take away the 5 black dots all at once, and then I can see I have 4 left without counting.

> I know 4 and 4 are doubles that make 8, so 8 − 4 = 4.

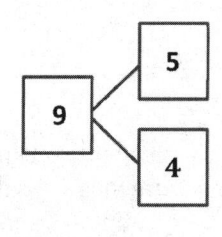

9 − 5 = __4__

9 − __4__ = 5

> I can imagine my 5-group drawing with 5 black dots and 3 white dots. That's 8.

3. Solve. Visualize your 5-groups to help you.

8 − __5__ = 3

> If I imagine 8, there is a group of 5 and a group of 3.

__8__ − 3 = 5

Lesson 35: Relate subtraction facts involving fives and doubles to corresponding decompositions.

141

A STORY OF UNITS – TEKS EDITION — Lesson 35 Homework Helper — 1•1

4. Complete the number sentence and number bond for each problem.

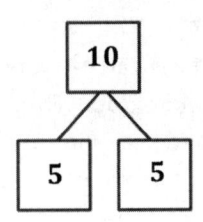

```
      10
     /  \
    5    5
```

10 - 5 = __5__

5. Match the number sentence to the strategy that helps you solve.

7 - __2__ = 5

6 - __3__ = 3

doubles

5-groups

I can imagine my 5-group drawing. 7 is made with a group of 5 and a group of 2. The missing part is 2. I'll draw a line to the 5-groups box.

The 5-group that makes 6 is 5 and 1. That won't help me much. Let me think of the double that makes 6... 3 and 3. Yes, 6 – 3 is 3. Doubles helped me solve this problem. I'll draw a line to the doubles box.

Lesson 35: Relate subtraction facts involving fives and doubles to corresponding decompositions.

Lesson 35 Homework 1•1

Write the number sentence and number bond for each problem.

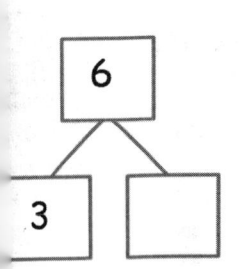

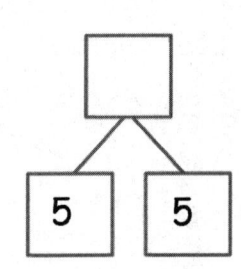

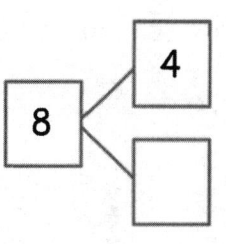

7.
```
    6
   / \
  3   ☐
```
8.
```
    ☐
   / \
  5   5
```
9.
```
    8
   / \
  ☐   4
```

6 - 3 = ___   ___ - 5 = 5   8 - ___ = 4

Match the number sentence to the strategy that helps you solve.

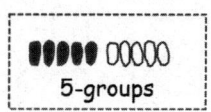

a. 7 - ___ = 2   doubles

b. 8 - ___ = 3   5-groups

c. 10 - ___ = 5   5-groups

d. ___ - 3 = 3   doubles

e. 8 - ___ = 4   5-groups

f. 9 - ___ = 5   doubles

Lesson 35: Relate subtraction facts involving fives and doubles to corresponding decompositions.

A STORY OF UNITS – TEKS EDITION

Name _____ Date _____

Solve the sets of number sentences. Look for easy groups to cro[ss]

1.

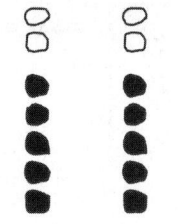

7 - 5 = ___

7 - 2 = ___

2.

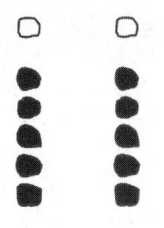

6 - 5 = ___

6 - 1 = ___

3.

9

9

Subtract. Make a math drawing for each problem like the ones [on] a number bond.

4.

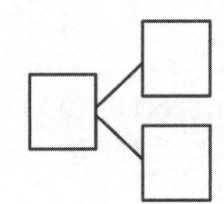

10 - 5 = ___

5.

8 - 5 = ___

8 - ___ =

6. Solve. Visualize 5-groups to help you.

a. 9 - ___ = 4   b. ___ - 5 = 5   c.

d. ___ - 5 = 2   e. ___ - 5 = 3   f.

Lesson 35: Relate subtraction facts involving fives and doubles to corres[ponding] decompositions.

A STORY OF UNITS – TEKS EDITION

Lesson 36 Homework Helper   1•1

1. Solve the sets of number sentences. Look for easy groups to cross off.

   > I can find the 6 in 10 really easily. 6 is made of 5 black dots and 1 white dot. I can cross that off all at once. That leaves me with 4.
   > 10 – 6 = 4.

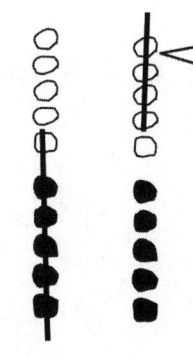

   > To take away the other part, I can cross off 4 from the end. That would leave me with 6. 10 – 4 = 6.

   10 – 6 = __4__

   __10__ – __6__ = __4__

2. Subtract. Then write the related subtraction sentence. Make a math drawing if needed, and complete the number bond for each.

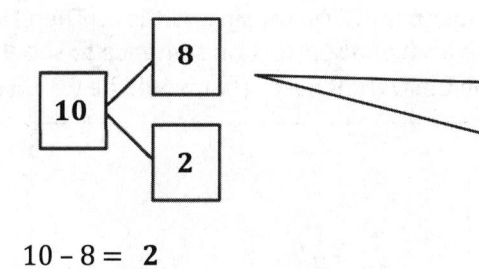

   Number bond: 10 → 8, 2

   10 – 8 = __2__

   10 – 2 = 8

   > I don't need to make a math drawing. I know that 8 and 2 make 10. In my number bond, I know the total is 10 and the two parts are 8 and 2. To write my related subtraction sentence, I need to subtract the other part. 10 – 2 = 8.

Lesson 36: Relate subtraction from 10 to corresponding decompositions.

145

A STORY OF UNITS – TEKS EDITION

Lesson 36 Homework Helper 1•1

3. Complete the number sentence and number bond for each problem. Match the number bond to the related subtraction problem. Write the other related subtraction number sentence.

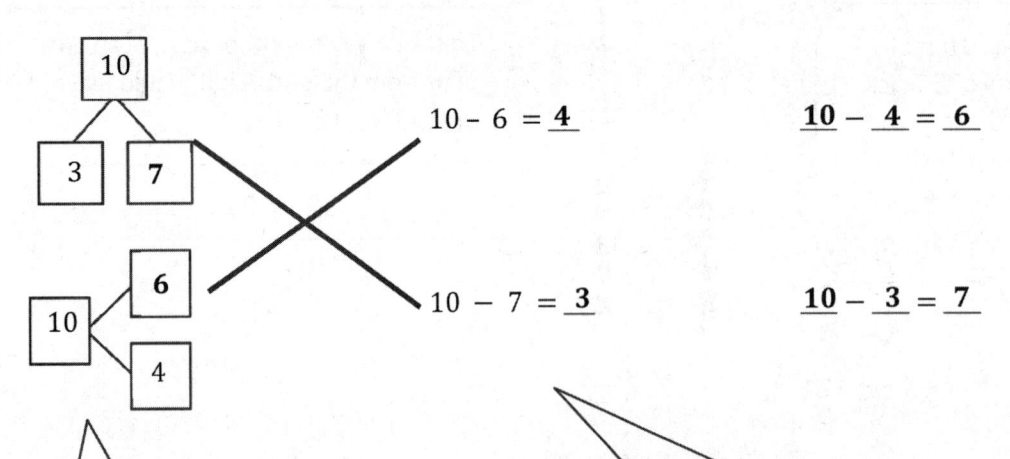

Number bond 1: 10 → 3, 7

Number bond 2: 10 → 6, 4

10 − 6 = __4__   10 − __4__ = __6__

10 − 7 = __3__   10 − __3__ = __7__

> I know my partners to 10. 3 and 7 make 10. 4 and 6 make 10.

> I have to look for the subtraction sentence that is taking away a part. I can match 10 − 7 with the first number bond. The missing part is 3. Then I will write a second subtraction sentence to show taking away the OTHER part. That would be 10 − 3 = 7.

Lesson 36: Relate subtraction from 10 to corresponding decompositions.

Name _____   Date _____

Make a math drawing, and solve. Use the first number sentence to help you write a related number sentence that matches your picture.

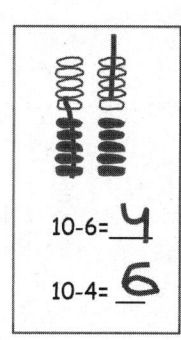

10-6= 4
10-4= 6

1.

10 - 2 = _____

___ - ___ = ___

2.

10 - 1 = _____

___ - ___ = ___

3.

10 - 7 = _____

___ - ___ = ___

Subtract. Then, write the related subtraction sentence. Make a math drawing if needed, and complete a number bond for each.

4.

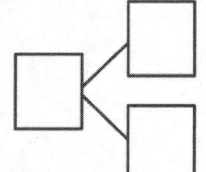

10 - 2 = ___

_____

5.

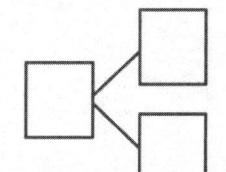

10 - ___ = 9

_____

6.

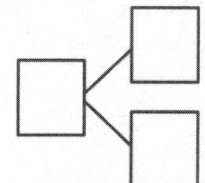

10 - ___ = 6

_____

7.

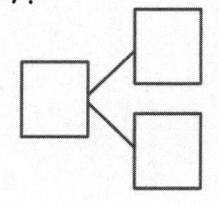

10 - ___ = 1

_____

8.

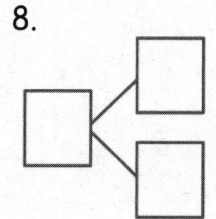

___ = 10 - 5

_____

A STORY OF UNITS – TEKS EDITION						Lesson 36 Homework 1•1

9. Complete the number bond. Match the number bond to the related subtraction sentence. Write the other related subtraction number sentence.

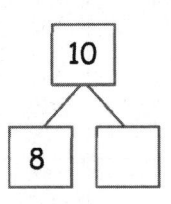

a. [10; 8, __]

10 - 5 = _____   ___ - ___ = ___

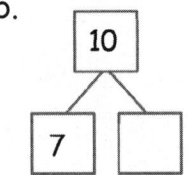

b. [10; 7, __]

10 - 1 = _____   ___ - ___ = ___

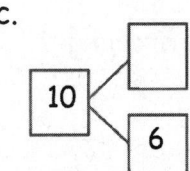

c. [10; __, 6]

10 - 2 = _____   ___ - ___ = ___

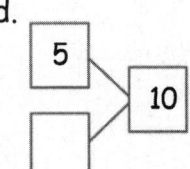

d. [__, __; 10] (parts 5 and __, whole 10)

10 - 4 = _____   ___ - ___ = ___

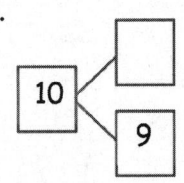

e. [10; __, 9]

10 - 3 = _____   ___ - ___ = ___

A STORY OF UNITS – TEKS EDITION

Lesson 38 Homework Helper 1•1

Find and solve the addition problems that are doubles and 5-groups.

Make subtraction flashcards for the related subtraction facts. (Remember, doubles will only make 1 related subtraction fact instead of 2 related facts.)

Make a number bond card, and use your cards to play Memory.

5 + 0	5 + 1	5 + 2	5 + 3	5 + 4	5 + 5
6 + 0	6 + 1	6 + 2	6 + 3	6 + 4	
7 + 0	7 + 1	7 + 2	7 + 3		
8 + 0	8 + 1	8 + 2			
9 + 0	9 + 1				
10 + 0					

> 5 + 5 = 10 is a double fact and uses a 5-group. Both addends are 5.

> 5 + 4 uses a 5-group since 5 is one of the addends. I'll make the subtraction flashcards 9 − 5 = 4 and 9 − 4 = 5. This row has more facts that use a 5-group.

5 + 4 = 9

9 − 4 = 5

9 − 5 = 4

> 5 and 4 are the parts that make 9.

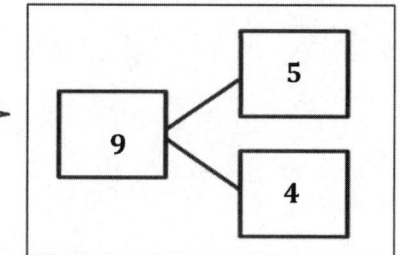

Number bond: 9 → 5 and 4

Lesson 38: Look for and make use of repeated reasoning and structure using the addition chart to solve subtraction problems.

153

9. Use 5-group drawings to help you complete the number bond. Match the number bond to the related subtraction sentence. Write the other related subtraction number sentence.

a. 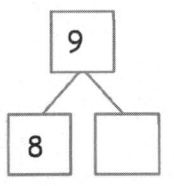
9 / 8, ___

9 - 5 = _____   ___ - ___ = ___

b.
9 / 7, ___

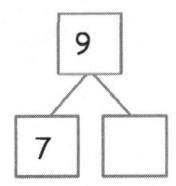

9 - 1 = _____   ___ - ___ = ___

c. 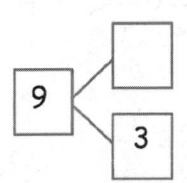
9 / ___, 3

9 - 2 = _____   ___ - ___ = ___

d.
5, ___ / 9

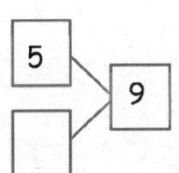

9 - 6 = _____   ___ - ___ = ___

e. 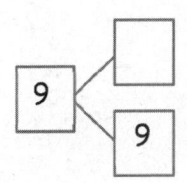
9 / ___, 9

9 - ___ = 0   ___ - ___ = ___

Name _____   Date _____

Make 5-group drawings and solve. Use the first number sentence to help you write a related number sentence that matches your picture.

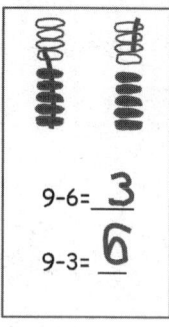

1.   2.   3.

9 - 6 = 3
9 - 3 = 6

9 - 2 = ___   9 - 8 = ___   9 - 4 = ___

___ - ___ = ___   ___ - ___ = ___   ___ - ___ = ___

Subtract. Then, write the related subtraction sentence. Make a math drawing if needed, and complete a number bond for each.

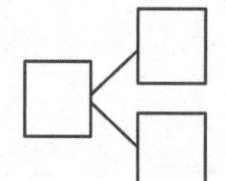

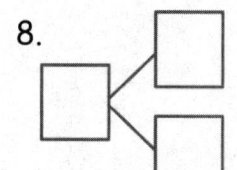

4. 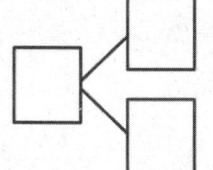   5.   6.

9 - 7 = ___   9 - ___ = 9   9 - ___ = 6

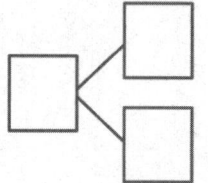

_____   _____   _____

7. 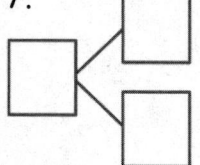   8.

9 - ___ = 1   ___ = 9 - 5

_____   _____

Lesson 37: Relate subtraction from 9 to corresponding decompositions.

A STORY OF UNITS – TEKS EDITION

Lesson 37 Homework Helper   1•1

1. Make 5-group drawings and solve. Use the first number sentence to help you write a related number sentence that matches your picture.

> I can find the 6 in 9 really easily. 6 is made of 5 black dots and 1 white dot. I can cross that off all at once. That leaves me with 3.
> 9 – 6 = 3.

> To take away the other part, I can cross off 3 from the end. That would leave me with 6. 9 – 3 = 6.

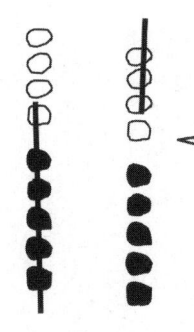

$$9 - 6 = \underline{3}$$
$$\underline{9} - \underline{3} = \underline{6}$$

2. Subtract. Then, write the related subtraction sentence. Make a math drawing if needed, and complete the number bond for each.

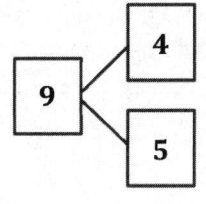

Number bond: 9 → 4, 5

> I don't need to make a math drawing. I know that 5 and 4 make 9. In my number bond, I know the total is 9 and the two parts are 4 and 5. To write my related subtraction sentence, I need to subtract the other part. 9 – 5 = 4.

$$9 - 4 = \underline{5}$$
$$\underline{9} - \underline{5} = \underline{4}$$

Lesson 37: Relate subtraction from 9 to corresponding decompositions.

A STORY OF UNITS – TEKS EDITION
Lesson 37 Homework Helper 1•1

3. Use 5-group drawings to help you complete the number bond. Match the number bond to the related subtraction problem. Write the other related subtraction number sentence.

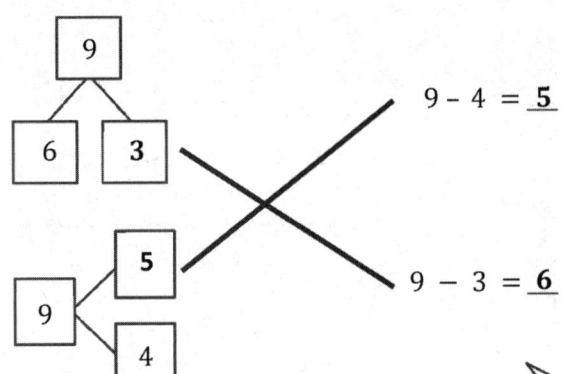

Number bond: 9 → 6 and 3

Number bond: 9 → 5 and 4

9 − 4 = **5**   **9** − **5** = **4**

9 − 3 = **6**   **9** − **6** = **3**

> I can think of my 5-group drawings to help me. When I picture 9 and I take out 4, that leaves me with 5. I could make a drawing if I want, but I don't need to. 9 is made of 5 and 4.

> I have to look for the subtraction sentence that is taking away a part. I can match 9 − 3 with the first number bond. The missing part is 6. Then I will write a second subtraction sentence to show taking away the OTHER part. That would be 9 − 6 = 3.

Lesson 37: Relate subtraction from 9 to corresponding decompositions.

Name _____   Date _____

Find and solve the 7 unshaded addition problems that are doubles and 5-groups.

Make subtraction flashcards for the related subtraction facts. (Remember, doubles will only make 1 related subtraction fact instead of 2 related facts.)

Make a number bond card and use your cards to play Memory.

1 + 0	1 + 1	1 + 2	1 + 3	1 + 4	1 + 5	1 + 6	1 + 7	1 + 8	1 + 9
2 + 0	2 + 1	2 + 2	2 + 3	2 + 4	2 + 5	2 + 6	2 + 7	2 + 8	
3 + 0	3 + 1	3 + 2	3 + 3	3 + 4	3 + 5	3 + 6	3 + 7		
4 + 0	4 + 1	4 + 2	4 + 3	4 + 4	4 + 5	4 + 6			
5 + 0	5 + 1	5 + 2	5 + 3	5 + 4	5 + 5				
6 + 0	6 + 1	6 + 2	6 + 3	6 + 4					
7 + 0	7 + 1	7 + 2	7 + 3						
8 + 0	8 + 1	8 + 2							
9 + 0	9 + 1								
10 + 0									

Lesson 38: Look for and make use of repeated reasoning and structure using the addition chart to solve subtraction problems.

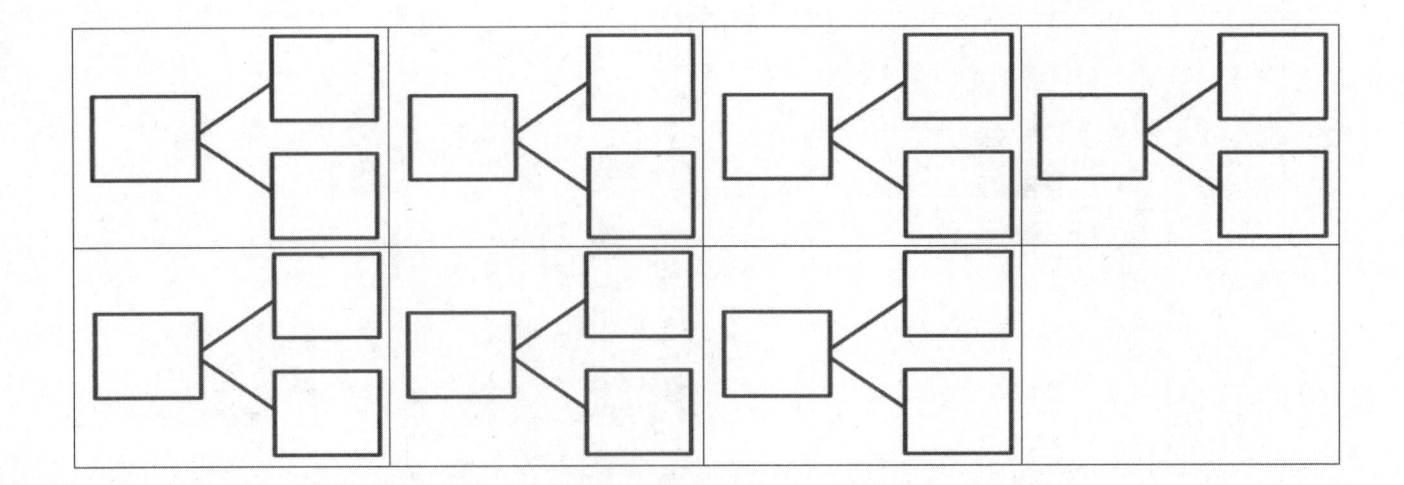

A STORY OF UNITS – TEKS EDITION   Lesson 39 Homework Helper   1•1

Solve the unshaded addition problems below. Write the two subtraction facts that would have the same number bond. To help you practice your addition and subtraction facts even more, make your own number bond flash cards.

5 + 0	5 + 1	5 + 2	5 + 3	5 + 4	5 + 5
6 + 0	6 + 1	6 + 2	6 + 3	6 + 4	
7 + 0	7 + 1	7 + 2	7 + 3		
8 + 0	8 + 1	8 + 2			
9 + 0	9 + 1				
10 + 0					

7 + 2 is 9. I can make two subtraction sentences, starting with the total of 9.

9 − 7 = 2 and 9 − 2 = 7.

| 9 − 7 = 2 | 9 − 2 = 7 |
| 10 − 7 = 3 | 10 − 3 = 7 |

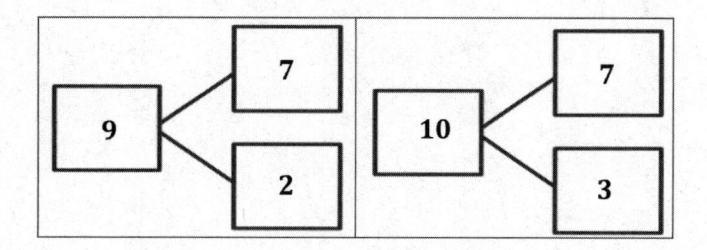

Number bonds: 9 with parts 7 and 2; 10 with parts 7 and 3.

Lesson 39: Analyze the addition chart to create sets of related addition and subtraction facts.

A STORY OF UNITS – TEKS EDITION

Lesson 39 Homework 1•1

Nombre _____   Fecha _____

Solve the unshaded addition problems below.

1 + 0	1 + 1	1 + 2	1 + 3	1 + 4	1 + 5	1 + 6	1 + 7	1 + 8	1 + 9
2 + 0	2 + 1	2 + 2	2 + 3	2 + 4	2 + 5	2 + 6	2 + 7	2 + 8	
3 + 0	3 + 1	3 + 2	3 + 3	3 + 4	3 + 5	3 + 6	3 + 7		
4 + 0	4 + 1	4 + 2	4 + 3	4 + 4	4 + 5	4 + 6			
5 + 0	5 + 1	5 + 2	5 + 3	5 + 4	5 + 5				
6 + 0	6 + 1	6 + 2	6 + 3	6 + 4					
7 + 0	7 + 1	7 + 2	7 + 3						
8 + 0	8 + 1	8 + 2							
9 + 0	9 + 1								
10 + 0									

4 + 2

Pick an addition fact from the chart. Use the grid to write the two subtraction facts that would have the same number bond. Repeat in order to make a set of subtraction flash cards. To help you practice your addition and subtraction facts even more, make your own number bond flash cards with the templates on the last page.

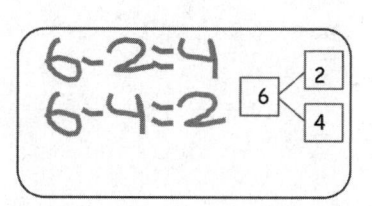

6 - 2 = 4
6 - 4 = 2

Lesson 39: Analyze the addition chart to create sets of related addition and subtraction facts.

Lesson 39 Homework 1•1

Lesson 39: Analyze the addition chart to create sets of related addition and subtraction facts.

Lesson 39 Homework

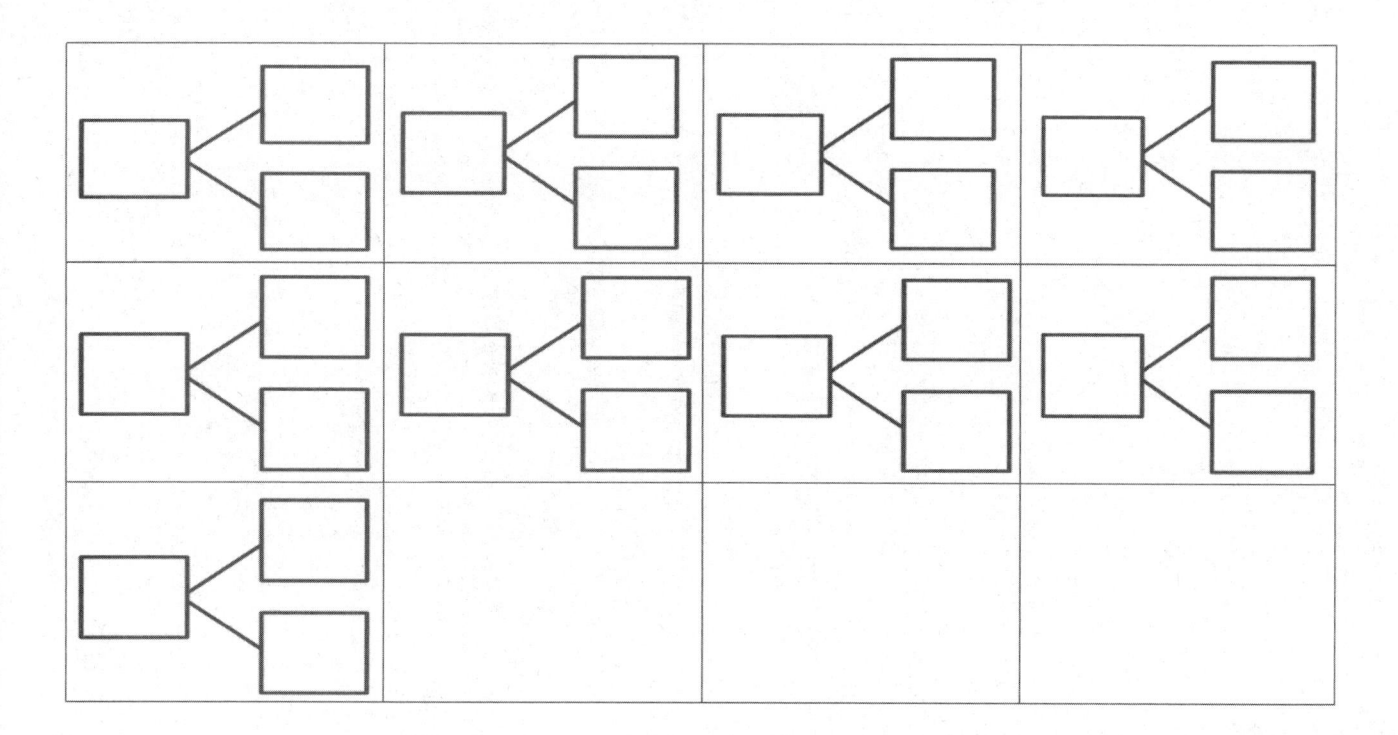